WORLD GEOGRAPHY TODAY
TEST GENERATOR · TEST ITEM LISTING

HOLT, RINEHART AND WINSTON
Harcourt Brace & Company

Austin • New York • Orlando • Chicago • Atlanta • San Francisco • Boston • Dallas • Toronto • London

Printed in the United States of America

ISBN 0-03-095195-X

2 3 4 5 6   066   98 97 96 95 94

Contents

About World Geography Today Test Generator

The *World Geography Today Test Generator* contains twenty-five test items for each chapter and unit of your textbook. For your easy reference, this *Test Item Listing* contains a complete printout of the test generator questions that are stored on the Test Items Disks. It also contains information that is specific to the use of the program with those questions.

The *User's Guide* which is included in the test generator package contains directions for installing the program and for using it.

Question Attributes

The test questions are stored in chapter files. There is a file for each chapter and unit of your textbook. In addition, each test item is classified by its question type and objective code. These are called attributes. The test generator lets you use attributes when you select questions for a test. It also allows you to view and to change question attributes. Your *User's Guide* describes these features of the program.

Question Types

The *World Geography Today Test Generator* has four question types stored on the Test Items Disks. When the program displays information about a question, it uses a one-letter abbreviation for the question type.

Question Types and Codes

Matching	**K**	Short Answer	**S**
Multiple Choice	**M**	Critical Thinking	**X**

Objectives

Each question has an objective code that ties the question to one of the objectives stated in the teacher's edition. Section objectives in the teacher's edition are located at the beginning of each section's lesson cycle; unit objectives can be found in the side column of each unit opener.

The objective code consists of two digits. In the case of the chapter test items, the first digit represents one of the sections of the chapter and the second digit represents an objective for that section. For example, if a question in the file for Chapter Five has an objective code of 23, the question covers the third objective in section two of the chapter. In the case of the unit test items, the first digit of the objective code represents the unit being tested and the second digit corresponds to an objective for that unit. For example, if a question in the file for Unit 8 has an objective code of 85, the question covers the fifth objective of Unit 8.

Technical Support

If you have any questions about the test generator or need assistance, call the Holt, Rinehart and Winston Technical Support Line at 1-800-323-9239.

CHAPTER 1

TEST QUESTIONS

Matching

Match the term with its correct description. One term is not used.

a. absolute location
b. topographic
c. cartography
d. region
e. relative location
f. environmental

1. Relating to surface features

2. The position of a place in relation to other places

3. An area defined by common characteristics

4. The branch of geography that is concerned with maps and mapmaking

5. The exact site on Earth where something is found

Match the term with its correct description. One term is not used.

g. situation
h. spatial interaction
i. human geography
j. drought
k. site
l. meteorology

6. The movement of people, goods, and ideas from one place to another

7. The study of how people and their activities vary from place to place

8. The field of geography that specializes in weather and weather forecasting

9. A relative location

10. A long, dry period with no rain

Multiple Choice

Circle the letter of the <u>best</u> answer.

11. A geographer might study all of the following except
    a. the movement of people, materials, and ideas across Earth's surface.
    b. how people interact with their environment.
    c. the origins of the sun and earth.
    d. how the earth's natural features vary from place to place.

12. A new high school is two blocks away from a bus stop and one mile from downtown. This is an example of
   a. region.
   b. relative location.
   c. movement.
   d. topography.

13. Geographers studying human-environment interaction in Africa's Sahel region might focus on
   a. local religious beliefs.
   b. agricultural practices in the region.
   c. the education of African students.
   d. local medical problems.

14. Geographers use the concept of region to
   a. divide the world into smaller areas for easier study.
   b. explain the origins of mountains.
   c. promote good citizenship.
   d. classify people in permanent categories.

15. The challenge faced by the National Park Service in Yosemite is to
   a. convince people to visit other national parks.
   b. find money to build more roads, hotels, and campgrounds in the park.
   c. encourage more tourists to visit Yosemite.
   d. maintain the park's environment as the number of visitors increases.

16. The Five Themes of Geography are useful because they
   a. define regions by describing their common characteristics.
   b. help people organize ideas about the world and its people.
   c. help geographers find solutions to social problems.
   d. do all of the above.

17. Geographers make decisions involving all of the following except
   a. environmental management.
   b. medical treatments.
   c. markets for businesses.
   d. transportation routes.

18. A geographer working in the field of human geography would most likely be interested in
   a. population studies.
   b. volcanic eruptions.
   c. climate patterns.
   d. desert ecology.

19. Computers have revolutionized map production by
   a. making maps more colorful.
   b. creating all new maps from scratch.
   c. combining old data with satellite photographs and other recent data.
   d. replacing cartographers with computer programmers.

20. A geographer who gathers and presents information about the weather is called a(n)
   a. meteorologist.
   b. topographer.
   c. environmentalist.
   d. cartographer.

Short Answer

Answer the questions in the space provided.

21. How does physical geography differ from human geography?
   _____
   _____
   _____
   _____
   _____

2

22. What is the difference between relative location and absolute location?

_____

_____

_____

_____

_____

Critical Thinking

Write your answers on a separate sheet of paper.

23. Describe the area in which you live in terms of the Five Themes of Geography.

24. Evaluate the use of the Five Themes of Geography as a tool for the study of physical and human geography.

25. How does the presence of skyscrapers and underground transportation in cities show how people have adapted the environment to meet their needs?

CHAPTER 1

TEST ANSWERS

Matching

1. Answer: b Objective: 22

2. Answer: e Objective: 12

3. Answer: d Objective: 12

4. Answer: c Objective: 22

5. Answer: a Objective: 12

6. Answer: h Objective: 12

7. Answer: i Objective: 21

8. Answer: l Objective: 22

9. Answer: g Objective: 12

10. Answer: j Objective: 11

Multiple Choice

11. Answer: c Objective: 11

12. Answer: b Objective: 12

13. Answer: b Objective: 11

14. Answer: a Objective: 12

15. Answer: d Objective: 11

16. Answer: d Objective: 12

17. Answer: b Objective: 22

18. Answer: a Objective: 21

19. Answer: c Objective: 22

20. Answer: a Objective: 22

Short Answer

21. Answer:
Physical geography is the study of the earth's natural features, while human geography is the study of how people and their activities vary throughout the world.

Objective: 21

22. Answer:
    Absolute location is the exact spot on Earth where something is found, while relative location is the position of a place in relation to other places.

    Objective: 12

Critical Thinking

23. Answer:
    Answers will vary depending on the characteristics of students' communities. Each student should describe his or her community's absolute location (its latitude and longitude) as well as its relative location, its human and physical characteristics, and how the community has adapted to or changed the environment to suit its needs. Students should also describe how people in their communities acquire the goods and services they need and how they travel from one place to another. Finally, they should identify common characteristics that make their communities regions or parts of larger regions.

    Objective: 12

24. Answer:
    Possible answer: The Five Themes of Geography make it possible to look at a particular situation from several perspectives. This increased understanding is helpful in the development of solutions to problems.

    Objective: 12

25. Answer:
    Possible answer: The availability of jobs and abundant goods and services make cities densely populated areas. Skyscrapers solve the problem of accommodating a large number of workers and residents in a limited area, as they occupy vertical, rather than horizontal, space. Many outside vehicles enter and leave cities every day. Underground transportation enables residents to travel quickly from one part of the city to another in spite of heavy traffic and the crowded conditions of their urban environment.

    Objective: 12

CHAPTER 2

TEST QUESTIONS

Matching

Match the term with its correct description. One term is not used.

a. revolution
b. equinox
c. planet
d. solstice
e. biosphere
f. rotation

1. A spherical object that revolves around a star

2. One complete spin of Earth on its axis

3. The time when Earth's axis points at its greatest angle toward or away from the sun

4. The time when Earth's axis is not pointed toward or away from the sun

5. A nearly circular orbit made by Earth around the sun

Match the term with its correct description. One term is not used.

g. hydrosphere
h. lithosphere
i. tropics
j. atmosphere
k. earth system
l. polar regions

6. Warm, low-latitude areas near the equator

7. The interactions of elements on and around the earth that work to create our physical environment

8. The layer of gases that surround the earth

9. Cold, high-latitude regions that receive little solar energy

10. All the water found in the oceans, on the land, and in the atmosphere

Multiple Choice

Circle the letter of the best answer.

11. When seen from Earth, the sun looks much larger than other stars because it is
    a. the largest star in the universe.
    b. reflecting light from Earth's moon.
    c. closer to Earth than other stars.
    d. the largest planet in the solar system.

12. A rotation of the earth takes one full day; a revolution, however, takes one
    a. night.   b. month.   c. year.   d. week.

13. The physical systems that make up the earth system
    a. are interrelated.
    b. do not affect plant and animal life.
    c. are found on all planets in the solar system.
    d. operate independently from each other.

14. The angle at which the sun's rays strike Earth determines the
    a. distance of Earth from the sun.
    b. seasons of the year.
    c. position of the sun in relation to Earth.
    d. speed of Earth's rotation.

15. The longest day of the year in the Northern Hemisphere occurs during the
    a. September equinox.   b. December solstice.
    c. March equinox.   d. June solstice.

16. During an equinox, the earth's axis is
    a. tilted at its greatest angle away from or toward the sun.
    b. not pointed away from or toward the sun.
    c. tilted 45° in relation to the sun.
    d. pointed straight up and down.

17. The physical system that contains all of Earth's animal and plant life is called the
    a. lithosphere.   b. hydrosphere.
    c. biosphere.   d. atmosphere.

18. You are planning a trip to Australia. If you want to sunbathe and swim in the ocean, it
    would be best to go during
    a. January.   b. May.   c. July.   d. October.

19. Earth is unique in the solar system because it is the only planet with
    a. four physical systems that support life.
    b. an orbit around the sun.
    c. natural satellites like the moon.
    d. southern and northern hemispheres.

20. Areas on the earth that receive constant sunlight during the December solstice are located
    south of the
    a. Arctic Circle.   b. Tropic of Cancer.
    c. Tropic of Capricorn.   d. Antarctic Circle.

Short Answer

Answer the questions in the space provided.

21. Define the earth system. What does it include?
    _____
    _____
    _____
    _____
    _____

22. Describe Earth's position within the solar system.
    _____
    _____
    _____
    _____
    _____

8

Critical Thinking

Write your answers on a separate sheet of paper.

23. Describe the three factors that control the amount of solar energy that reach different parts of Earth.

24. What would happen if Earth had no tilt? Explain your answer.

25. Could life exist on other planets? Could these planets be in our solar system? What conditions would be necessary for life to exist on these planets?

CHAPTER 2

TEST ANSWERS

Matching

1. Answer: c Objective: 11

2. Answer: f Objective: 12

3. Answer: d Objective: 22

4. Answer: b Objective: 22

5. Answer: a Objective: 12

6. Answer: i Objective: 21

7. Answer: k Objective: 31

8. Answer: j Objective: 32

9. Answer: l Objective: 21

10. Answer: g Objective: 32

Multiple Choice

11. Answer: c Objective: 11

12. Answer: c Objective: 12

13. Answer: a Objective: 31

14. Answer: b Objective: 22

15. Answer: d Objective: 22

16. Answer: b Objective: 22

17. Answer: c Objective: 32

18. Answer: a Objective: 22

19. Answer: a Objective: 32

20. Answer: d Objective: 22

Short Answer

21. Answer:
    The earth system is the interaction of elements within four physical systems that create Earth's physical environment: the atmosphere, the lithosphere, the hydrosphere, and the biosphere.

    Objective: 31

22. Answer:
The sun is located at the center of the solar system, which contains nine planets. Earth, one of the smaller planets, is the third nearest planet to the sun.

Objective: 11

Critical Thinking

23. Answer:
The three factors controlling the amount of solar energy that reach different parts of Earth are the planet's rotation, revolution, and tilt. Earth rotates around its axis. One rotation takes 24 hours. When we see the sun rising and setting, we are actually seeing the effects of Earth's eastward rotation. Only the half of the planet facing the sun receives solar energy, in the form of heat and light; thus the earth's rotation creates day and night.

The Earth makes one revolution, or orbit, around the sun every 365 1/4 days. The orbit is nearly circular, so Earth is nearly always the same distance from the sun. Tilt refers to the fact that the earth's axis leans in relation to the sun. When the North Pole is pointed away from the sun, the Southern Hemisphere receives more solar energy. When the North Pole is pointed toward the sun, the Northern Hemisphere receives more solar energy. Thus, the earth's tilt regulates the seasons.

Objective: 12

24. Answer:
The earth's tilt is one of the factors controlling the amount of the sun's energy that falls on various parts of Earth. If the earth's axis always pointed straight up and down in relation to the sun, every day would be the same length because light and darkness would be of equal duration everywhere. There would be exactly 12 hours of daylight and 12 hours of darkness. Also, if the earth did not lean away from or toward the sun during different positions of its orbit, then the amount of solar energy striking any spot on the earth's surface would never change. Therefore, the seasons, times of lesser or greater heat, would not occur.

Objective: 22

25. Answer:
Possible answer: Yes, life could exist on other planets. It could not exist on other planets in our solar system, however, for only Earth has the four physical systems necessary to life: an atmosphere, lithosphere, biosphere, and hydrosphere. Earth also has the advantage of not being too warm or too cold, unlike other planets in our solar system. Planets in other solar systems with similar physical systems could, theoretically, support life.

Objective: 32

CHAPTER 3

TEST QUESTIONS

Matching

Match the term with its correct description.   One term is not used.

a. air pressure
b. trade winds
c. precipitation
d. climate
e. temperature
f. doldrums

1. The movement of air from the subtropical high-pressure zone toward the equatorial low-pressure zone

2. Calm areas along the equator with no prevailing winds

3. The measurement of heat energy in the atmosphere

4. Condensed droplets of water that fall to Earth as rain, snow, sleet, and hail

5. The measurement of the force exerted by air

Match the term with its correct description.   One term is not used.

g. steppe
h. elevation
i. permafrost
j. monsoon
k. evaporation
l. humidity

6. The amount of water vapor in the air

7. A wind that blows for months from the same direction at the same time each year

8. The height on the earth's surface above or below sea level

9. The process by which water changes from a liquid to a gas

10. A condition in tundra regions where water below the surface remains frozen for most of the year

Multiple Choice

Circle the letter of the <u>best</u> answer.

11. The equatorial low-pressure zone is caused by
    a. constant cold sinking air.
    b. warm air sinking to the surface.
    c. warm air rising over the equator.
    d. cold air rising from the polar high-pressure zone.

12. The factor that most strongly influences a region's climate is
   a. latitude.   b. vegetation.
   c. condensation.   d. population.

13. The prevailing winds found in the high latitudes are the
   a. westerlies, which blow from west to east.
   b. trade winds, which blow toward the equator.
   c. jet streams, which move storms and major weather patterns.
   d. polar winds, which bring cold weather to the middle latitudes.

14. The most common type of storm on Earth is a
   a. hurricane.   b. typhoon.
   c. thunderstorm.   d. tornado.

15. Precipitation occurs immediately after
   a. air reaches a temperature at which it can hold no more water vapor.
   b. water vapor is evaporated from the oceans.
   c. water vapor changes from a gas to liquid droplets.
   d. condensed droplets become large enough to fall to Earth.

16. The leeward side of a mountain differs from the windward side in that it
   a. receives a great deal of moisture.
   b. always faces toward the ocean.
   c. has a much drier climate.
   d. receives warm, dry air flowing from the desert.

17. All dry climate regions share the feature of
   a. low annual rainfall.   b. consistent temperatures.
   c. high elevation.   d. short-grass vegetation.

18. The ocean-influenced climate in which temperatures are mild, winters are rainy, and summers are warm and sunny is the
   a. humid-continental climate.   b. marine-west-coast climate.
   c. Mediterranean climate.   d. subarctic climate.

19. The humid-tropical climate is characterized by
   a. long, sunny, dry summers and mild winters.
   b. alternating seasons of heavy rainfall and dryness.
   c. short, cool summers and long winters.
   d. warm temperatures and heavy rainfall year-round.

20. High-latitude climates are very cold because these areas
   a. are surrounded by oceans.
   b. are covered with tundra vegetation.
   c. receive little of the sun's energy.
   d. have a high elevation.

Short Answer

Answer the questions in the space provided.

21. Why don't hurricanes occur in the high latitudes?

   _____
   _____
   _____
   _____
   _____

14

22. Why does a warm humid day feel warmer than a dry day with the same temperature?

_____
_____
_____
_____
_____
_____

Critical Thinking

Write your answers on a separate sheet of paper.

23. Explain how air pressure, wind, and ocean circulation work to help the earth maintain an energy balance.

24. Explain the orographic effect and the rain-shadow effect.

25. Imagine that you are told that your area has a humid-continental climate. What weather characteristics might support this assertion? What might you conclude about the area's latitude and location relative to oceans?

CHAPTER 3

TEST ANSWERS

Matching

   1.Answer: b Objective: 11

   2.Answer: f Objective: 11

   3.Answer: e Objective: 12

   4.Answer: c Objective: 21

   5.Answer: a Objective: 11

   6.Answer: l Objective: 21

   7.Answer: j Objective: 31

   8.Answer: h Objective: 22

   9.Answer: k Objective: 21

  10.Answer: i Objective: 31

Multiple Choice

  11.Answer: c Objective: 11

  12.Answer: a Objective: 31

  13.Answer: d Objective: 12

  14.Answer: c Objective: 21

  15.Answer: d Objective: 21

  16.Answer: c Objective: 22

  17.Answer: a Objective: 32

  18.Answer: b Objective: 32

  19.Answer: d Objective: 32

  20.Answer: c Objective: 31

Short Answer

  21.Answer:
Storms occur under warm, low-pressure conditions in which unstable air is present. The high latitudes are in the polar high-pressure zones where constant cold sinking air keeps hurricanes from occurring.

Objective: 11

22.Answer:
   On a humid day, the air is already holding much moisture, or water vapor. Thus the air does not absorb as much moisture from a person's skin (perspiration) as dry air could. Since the evaporation of perspiration cools one's skin, a day when this evaporation is limited and occurs only slowly will feel warmer.

   Objective: 21

Critical Thinking

23.Answer:
   Air pressure creates the winds and ocean currents that make up the systems of global energy exchange. Differences in air pressure are caused when one part of the earth's surface is heated differently than another part. Unstable low-pressure areas develop where the earth is warmed. Warm air rises, is cooled, and forms clouds which may bring precipitation. High-pressure areas, which are stable, are found where cold air sinks and, in doing so, warms up.
   Wind results from the motion of air from high- to low-pressure areas. It flows from the ocean to land as a cool breeze as the land becomes warm, and from the land to the ocean as a cool breeze when the land cools at night. Wind helps Earth maintain an energy balance by moving heat and cold across the planet.
   Global wind belts, or prevailing winds, blow from areas of high pressure to areas of low pressure. Prevailing winds also set ocean currents in motion. These currents move water between the cold polar regions and the warm tropical regions, thus helping Earth maintain its energy balance in yet another way.

   Objective: 12

24.Answer:
   In the orographic effect, moist air flowing from the ocean is forced to rise when it meets a mountain barrier. The air cools as it rises, leading to condensation and precipitation in the form of rain or snow. The windward side of the mountain receives much moisture. The air then warms as it moves down the leeward side, and this side of the mountain is usually quite dry. Deserts are often found here. These areas are said to be in a rain shadow because they do not receive much rain.

   Objective: 22

25.Answer:
   Weather characteristics include changing weather conditions, four distinct seasons, extreme differences between summer and winter temperatures, and much rain and snow. The area is probably located in the middle latitudes and in the middle of a continent, away from oceans.

   Objective: 32

CHAPTER 4

TEST QUESTIONS

Matching

Match the term with its correct description. One term is not used.

a. hydroelectricity
b. watershed
c. industrialization
d. irrigation
e. wetlands
f. transpiration

  1. The watering of land through pipes, ditches, or canals

  2. The process by which plants give off water vapor through their leaves

  3. An area of land drained by a river and its tributaries

  4. A source of power produced when water stored behind dams drives engines

  5. Areas that are flooded for at least part of the year

Match the term with its correct description. One term is not used.

g. tributary
h. groundwater
i. continental shelf
j. hydrologic cycle
k. water table
l. estuary

  6. Fresh water found beneath the surface of the land, in tiny spaces between grains of soil and rock

  7. The circulation of water throughout the hydrosphere

  8. The shallowest part of the ocean

  9. A semi-enclosed coastal body of water where fresh water from rivers mixes with seawater

  10. A smaller stream or river that flows into a larger stream or river

Multiple Choice

Circle the letter of the <u>best</u> answer.

  11. Which of the following is a unique characteristic of water?
      a. It is the only substance that can exist as a liquid, solid, or gas.
      b. It heats and cools very quickly compared to other materials.
      c. It is found in all living and nonliving things.
      d. It is evenly distributed throughout the earth.

12. The three main steps of the hydrologic cycle are
    a. agriculture, irrigation, and industrialization.
    b. transpiration, perspiration, and evapotranspiration.
    c. the forming, joining, and draining of rivers.
    d. evaporation, condensation, and precipitation.

13. The majority of the hydrosphere is in the world's
    a. ice sheets.   b. oceans.
    c. lakes.   d. groundwater.

14. A layer of rock that can store and carry water is called
    a. a water table.   b. an aquifer.
    c. a hydrosphere.   d. a watershed.

15. The hydrologic cycle depends on solar energy because
    a. condensation cannot take place without sunlight.
    b. hydroelectricity cannot be produced without solar power.
    c. the water in aquifers is heated by the sun.
    d. heat from the sun evaporates water from the oceans.

16. The largest geographic feature on Earth is the
    a. Pacific Ocean.   b. Atlantic Ocean.
    c. Ogallala Aquifer.   d. Mississippi River.

17. Headwaters are formed
    a. by drainage from tributaries.
    b. when rivers meet an inlet of the sea.
    c. by runoff from precipitation.
    d. when land is irrigated.

18. A well to tap groundwater must be drilled
    a. to the bottom of the aquifer.
    b. to the top of the continental shelf.
    c. to a depth below the water table.
    d. in the middle of wetlands.

19. A major characteristic of seawater is that
    a. it contains many dissolved materials.
    b. it can easily be used for drinking water.
    c. the water is heated evenly at all depths.
    d. the temperature changes greatly from day to day.

20. The oceans support life
    a. evenly throughout their waters.
    b. mainly in warm, shallow areas.
    c. mainly in cold, deep areas.
    d. only in the paths of ocean currents.

Short Answer

Answer the questions in the space provided.

21. How are lakes formed?

    _____
    _____
    _____
    _____
    _____

22. What factors determine the depth of the water table?

_____
_____
_____
_____
_____
_____

Critical Thinking

Write your answers on a separate sheet of paper.

23. Why is water such a valuable resource for humans? Why is it important to conserve this resource and keep it clean?

24. How might the hydrosphere be affected if most of the earth's trees were cut down and not replaced?

25. What consequences might result from the destruction of the wetlands?

CHAPTER 4

TEST ANSWERS

Matching

1. Answer: d Objective: 11

2. Answer: f Objective: 13

3. Answer: b Objective: 21

4. Answer: a Objective: 11

5. Answer: e Objective: 21

6. Answer: h Objective: 22

7. Answer: j Objective: 13

8. Answer: i Objective: 23

9. Answer: l Objective: 21

10. Answer: g Objective: 21

Multiple Choice

11. Answer: a Objective: 12

12. Answer: d Objective: 13

13. Answer: b Objective: 13

14. Answer: b Objective: 22

15. Answer: d Objective: 13

16. Answer: a Objective: 23

17. Answer: c Objective: 21

18. Answer: c Objective: 22

19. Answer: a Objective: 23

20. Answer: b Objective: 23

Short Answer

21. Answer:
Most lakes are formed when runoff slows or stops and fills inland depressions on the land's surface. Many lakes, such as the Great Lakes in the United States and Canada, were formed by glaciers. Others have formed in the craters of erupted volcanoes.

Objective: 21

22. Answer:
The depth of the water table varies depending on how wet or dry the climate is, the shape of the land as it rises under hills and drops under valleys, annual rainfall patterns, and the number of wells in a region.

Objective: 22

Critical Thinking

23. Answer:
Possible answer: All living things are made up mostly of water, and water is essential for human survival. Not only do we need water to drink, water also makes up most of the foods we eat. Water is also important for many human activities. In dry climates, irrigation is necessary for growing crops. This is done with pipes, ditches, or canals in wealthier countries; some people in poorer countries depend on rain and water conservation for irrigation. In addition, industry could not function without water: water is the ingredient in the manufacture of many products, is a valuable power source, and is central to the world's transportation network. Finally, water is important for recreation and the quality of life. Water pollution affects plants and animals, threatening an important source of food. Clean water, which is becoming increasingly scarce, is necessary to life on Earth.

Objective: 11

24. Answer:
Possible answer: Although most water enters the atmosphere by evaporating from the oceans and other bodies of water, some water enters the atmosphere through transpiration, the giving off of water vapor by the leaves of plants. If trees were cut down and not replaced, some of the earth's water supply might not return to the atmosphere.

Objective: 13

25. Answer:
Possible answer: Many fish, shellfish, and birds that make wetlands their home could be threatened. Also, pollution might increase, as wetlands filter pollutants from water. Wetlands contain some of the most productive land in the world.

Objective: 21

CHAPTER 5

TEST QUESTIONS

Matching

Match the term with its correct description. One term is not used.

a. sediment
b. plate tectonics
c. relief
d. erosion
e. abyssal plains
f. subduction

1. Small particles of mud, sand, or gravel formed from broken rocks

2. The wearing away of land by forces such as wind, waves, and ice

3. A theory that explains how the world's large landforms were created

4. Large, smooth areas on the ocean floors

5. The process that takes place when a heavy plate collides with a lighter plate, dives under it, and sinks into the upper mantle

Match the term with its correct description. One term is not used.

g. alluvial fan
h. trench
i. mid-ocean ridge
j. glacier
k. plateau
l. floodplain

6. A landform created when mud and sand are deposited by a stream on the plain at a mountain's base

7. A chain of mountains on the ocean floor, formed at a plate boundary

8. A long, deep valley on the ocean floor, formed at a plate boundary

9. A mass of ice that moves across the earth's surface

10. A landform created by particles of rock, sand, or gravel deposited by a river or stream

Multiple Choice

Circle the letter of the <u>best</u> answer.

11. Rock weathering is the process that
    a. breaks up rocks and causes them to decay.
    b. causes sediment to be carried by water, wind, or ice.
    c. moves sand and dust from one place to another.
    d. takes place when two plates collide and their edges crumple.

12. You find a smooth, polished rock in a garden. This rock is most likely
    a. recently cooled lava.   b. a primary landform.
    c. part of the Earth's mantle.   d. a product of erosion.

13. According to the theory of plate tectonics, when plates move away from each other,
    a. continents are formed.
    b. a trench is created deep beneath the ocean floor.
    c. abyssal plains are created.
    d. a mid-ocean ridge is formed.

14. The Himalayas and Death Valley were both created by
    a. tectonic activity.   b. rock weathering.
    c. deposits of sediment.   d. volcanic eruptions.

15. Plains and plateaus are both examples of
    a. folding.   b. landforms.
    c. sand dunes.   d. plate boundaries.

16. The surface of the earth is bent and broken by
    a. glaciers pushing enormous rocks down mountains.
    b. the weathering of rocks by wind and water.
    c. volcanoes beneath the ocean floor.
    d. heat and rock movements in the crust and upper mantle.

17. A delta forms when
    a. plates slide past each other, making creases in the earth's surface.
    b. sediment is deposited at the base of a mountain.
    c. plates collide, lifting up mountains.
    d. mud and sand are carried from an alluvial fan to a river mouth and are deposited there.

18. Low, rounded mountains with wide valleys are
    a. tectonic plateaus.   b. primary landforms.
    c. hardened sediment.   d. secondary landforms.

19. Mountain ranges are often found in coastal areas because
    a. they are a continuation of the mountain chain under the ocean.
    b. erosion does not take place along the coast.
    c. coastal areas are often the sites of plate boundaries.
    d. these are the most inactive areas of the earth's surface.

20. Scientists believe that the continents formed when
    a. a meteor collided with Earth, breaking up the Americas into two continents.
    b. a supercontinent named Pangaea broke into smaller continents that drifted apart on plates.
    c. massive glaciers moved across the earth, breaking up the landmasses.
    d. lava cooled from volcanoes on the ocean floor.

Short Answer

Answer the questions in the space provided.

21. What are the three types of plate boundaries?
    _____
    _____
    _____
    _____
    _____

22. What is the difference between primary and secondary landforms?

_____
_____
_____
_____
_____

Critical Thinking

Write your answers on a separate sheet of paper.

23. What forces on and within the earth's surface give mountains their shape?

24. What would the earth look like if primary landforms were no longer being created?

25. Would you rather live near a plate boundary or in the center of a plate? Why?

CHAPTER 5

TEST ANSWERS

Matching

1.Answer: a Objective: 11

2.Answer: d Objective: 11

3.Answer: b Objective: 21

4.Answer: e Objective: 22

5.Answer: f Objective: 21

6.Answer: g Objective: 32

7.Answer: i Objective: 22

8.Answer: h Objective: 22

9.Answer: j Objective: 11

10.Answer: l Objective: 32

Multiple Choice

11.Answer: a Objective: 11

12.Answer: d Objective: 11

13.Answer: d Objective: 22

14.Answer: a Objective: 22

15.Answer: b Objective: 32

16.Answer: d Objective: 12

17.Answer: d Objective: 32

18.Answer: d Objective: 31

19.Answer: c Objective: 22

20.Answer: b Objective: 21

Short Answer

21.Answer:
The three types of plate boundaries are those where plates slide past each other, those where plates move away from each other, and those where plates push against each other.
Objective: 22

22. Answer:

Primary landforms are large masses of rock raised by volcanic eruptions and other forces, such as the collision of plates. Secondary landforms develop from primary landforms as erosion works on them.

Objective: 31

Critical Thinking

23. Answer:

Forces on and within the earth's surface work together to give mountains their shape. Mountains may begin as primary landforms formed by volcanic eruptions, faulting, folding, and other forces beneath the earth's surface. Rock weathering and erosion wear down the surface of mountains and transform them into secondary landforms. Water flowing down a mountain can eventually create gullies, valleys, and canyons. Mountain glaciers create sharp peaks and deep valleys.

Objective: 12

24. Answer:

Possible answer: Erosion would probably wear down all mountains. Eventually, without new mountains being created, the landscape would be smooth.

Objective: 31

25. Answer:

Answers will vary. Many human settlements near plate boundaries, such as those along the west coast of the United States, are at risk for earthquakes or volcanic activity. Those at the center of a plate are unlikely to experience severe tectonic activity.

Objective: 22

CHAPTER 6

TEST QUESTIONS

Matching

Match the term with its correct description. One term is not used.

a. climax community
b. photosynthesis
c. deciduous
d. savanna
e. ecosystem
f. humus

  1. Decayed plant or animal matter in soil

  2. A community of plants and animals that functions as a unit with the water, soil, and climate of a region

  3. A type of tree that loses its leaves at a certain season every year

  4. A tropical grassland with scattered trees and shrubs

  5. In plants, the conversion of sunlight into chemical energy

Match the term with its correct description. One term is not used.

g. coral reef
h. biome
i. plant succession
j. soil horizon
k. food chain
l. leaching

  6. The process by which one group of plants replaces another

  7. A series of organisms in which energy is passed along through living things

  8. The process by which nutrients necessary for plant growth are washed out of the topsoil by heavy rain

  9. A limestone ridge formed from the skeletons of tiny marine animals and found in shallow tropical water

  10. A plant and animal community that covers a large land area

Multiple Choice

Circle the letter of the <u>best</u> answer.

  11. The type of soil in a particular location is primarily determined by
      a. climate.   b. succession.
      c. leaching.   d. photosynthesis.

12. Plants are important for sustaining life on Earth because they are
    a. fewer in number than any other type of living thing.
    b. a source of carbon dioxide.
    c. at the top of the food chain.
    d. a source of oxygen.

13. The final stage of plant succession is called
    a. a mixed forest.   b. a climax community.
    c. an ecosystem.   d. a biome.

14. All of the following help many desert plants survive except
    a. the ability to store water.
    b. the ability to do without large quantities of water.
    c. the ability to absorb water from plants growing nearby.
    d. the ability to keep seeds alive underground for long periods between rains.

15. Bacteria and insects
    a. produce space between soil particles for gases and water.
    b. produce humus, which is needed for plant growth.
    c. prevent gases and minerals from entering the soil.
    d. break down particles of rock in the soil.

16. The soil horizon in which most plant roots are located is called
    a. solid rock.   b. broken rock.
    c. topsoil.   d. subsoil.

17. The forest biome that sustains dense plant growth all year long is the
    a. Mediterranean scrub forest. b. boreal forest.
    c. middle-latitude forest.   d. tropical rain forest.

18. Grassland biomes are located between the temperate forests and the
    a. savanna biomes.   b. desert biomes.
    c. tropical rain forests.   d. polar regions.

19. Deserts and boreal forests are similar in that both
    a. experience extensive leaching of the soil.
    b. are found in northern Europe and Asia.
    c. have plants that thrive in spite of extreme temperatures.
    d. cover less than 3 percent of the earth's land surface.

20. The living things found at the bottom of the food chain are
    a. insects.   b. plants.
    c. human beings.   d. birds.

Short Answer

Answer the questions in the space provided.

21. How do plants depend on other plants to grow?

    _____
    _____
    _____
    _____
    _____

22. What is the difference between coniferous and deciduous forests?

    _____
    _____
    _____
    _____
    _____

Critical Thinking

Write your answers on a separate sheet of paper.

23. Identify the five basic world biomes, and describe their characteristics.

24. How might the widening of a highway in a forested or grassy area affect plant succession?

25. Why are the savanna and desert biomes expanding more than any other biomes? What do you think can be done to stop the shrinking of the forest biome?

CHAPTER 6

TEST ANSWERS

Matching

1. Answer: f Objective: 12

2. Answer: e Objective: 11

3. Answer: c Objective: 22

4. Answer: d Objective: 21

5. Answer: b Objective: 11

6. Answer: i Objective: 11

7. Answer: k Objective: 13

8. Answer: l Objective: 12

9. Answer: g Objective: 13

10. Answer: h Objective: 21

Multiple Choice

11. Answer: a Objective: 12

12. Answer: d Objective: 11

13. Answer: b Objective: 11

14. Answer: c Objective: 22

15. Answer: a Objective: 12

16. Answer: c Objective: 12

17. Answer: d Objective: 21

18. Answer: b Objective: 21

19. Answer: c Objective: 22

20. Answer: b Objective: 13

Short Answer

21. Answer:
    Trees provide shade for plants that cannot endure direct sunlight. Plants also hold the soil in place and shelter the seeds of other plants. When plants die, they are broken down into nutrients in the soil, which other plants can then use.

    Objective: 11

22. Answer:

The trees in deciduous forests lose their leaves during a certain season each year, whereas trees in coniferous forests do not lose their leaves and remain green year-round.

Objective: 22

Critical Thinking

23. Answer:

The five biomes found throughout the world are forest, savanna, grassland, desert, and tundra. The forest biome is covered with trees. It includes tropical rain forests, temperate forests, boreal forests, and scrub forests. The savanna biome is a tropical grassland with scattered shrubs and trees located between tropical rain forests and deserts. The grassland biome is located between the temperate forests and the desert biomes; it can have the high grass of a prairie or the short-grass vegetation of a steppe. Desert biomes are found in the low and middle latitudes. Plants in these biomes use very little water or store water. The tundra biome, found in high latitudes and at high elevations, is very cold most of the year and does not support much plant life.

Objective: 21

24. Answer:

Possible answer: When a highway is widened, trees are cut down and other vegetation is removed. Concrete and asphalt will make it impossible for plants to return. Though the adjacent plant community has been disturbed, it may recover.

Objective: 11

25. Answer:

Possible answer: The savanna and desert biomes expand as forest biomes are cleared for farming by an increasing human population. As a result of farming and overgrazing, forest soil loses its nutrients and can no longer sustain plant growth.

Students might suggest several solutions to the problem, including land conservation, tree replanting, and economic incentives for farmers to plant crops and graze their animals elsewhere.

Objective: 22

UNIT 1

TEST QUESTIONS

Matching

Match the term with its correct description. One term is not used.

a. landforms
b. alluvial fan
c. climax community
d. front
e. westerlies
f. delta

1. The final stage of plant succession, in which a stable group of plants develops

2. A meeting zone of two air masses with different temperatures and amounts of moisture

3. Shapes on the earth's surface

4. Prevailing winds that blow from west to east across the middle latitudes

5. Deposits of sediment at a river mouth

Match the term with its correct description. One term is not used.

g. weather
h. condensation
i. biome
j. evapotranspiration
k. region
l. solar system

6. The condition of the atmosphere at a given place and time

7. The process by which water vapor is returned to the atmosphere from the land and from plants

8. A plant and animal community that covers a large land area

9. The sun and the nine planets, including Earth, that revolve around it

10. An area defined by common characteristics

Multiple Choice

Circle the letter of the <u>best</u> answer.

11. The three factors that control the amount of the sun's energy received on Earth are
    a. groundwater, elevation, and population.
    b. rotation, revolution, and tilt.
    c. irrigation, climate, and precipitation.
    d. wind, photosynthesis, and plant succession.

12. The climate type that lies closest to the equator is the
    a. humid-tropical climate.   b. tundra climate.
    c. marine-west-coast climate.   d. humid-continental climate.

13. A food chain is a series of steps in which
    a. energy is passed in different forms through living things.
    b. water is circulated throughout the hydrosphere.
    c. soil is enriched to sustain plant growth.
    d. plant communities become climax communities.

14. The continents, volcanoes, and some mountains were probably created by
    a. erosion and sedimentation.
    b. plate tectonics.
    c. the orographic and rain-shadow effects.
    d. the hydrologic cycle.

15. A cartographer would be most likely to
    a. analyze North American weather patterns.
    b. write an article explaining the Five Themes of Geography.
    c. create a map of world climate regions.
    d. advise a gas company about where to drill for oil.

16. Forest biomes are found
    a. only in humid-tropical climate regions.
    b. at various latitudes and in different climate regions.
    c. between desert biomes and savanna biomes.
    d. only at high elevations.

17. The geography theme that best describes the hydrologic cycle is
    a. location.   b. region.
    c. human-environment interaction. d. movement.

18. Regions that share the same biome type also
    a. have similar climates.
    b. have the largest populations.
    c. are located at high elevations.
    d. have identical landforms.

19. If you lived on the windward side of a coastal mountain range, you would probably experience
    a. the rain-shadow effect.   b. uncrowded living conditions.
    c. frequent earthquakes.   d. a moist climate.

20. Geographers do all of the following except
    a. help preserve the earth's natural environments.
    b. assist governments with problems related to droughts and other weather conditions.
    c. pass laws designed to improve schools in rural areas of the country.
    d. work with businesses to identify new markets.

Short Answer

Answer the questions in the space provided.

21. How does Earth maintain an energy balance?
    _____
    _____
    _____
    _____
    _____

22. What are the Five Themes of Geography? Why are they useful to geographers?

_____
_____
_____
_____
_____

Critical Thinking

Write your answers on a separate sheet of paper.

23. How does the earth's physical geography determine where and how people live?

24. How would the earth's physical geography be affected if its oceans were smaller?

25. If you were a geographer, would you be most interested in researching climate, landforms, plate tectonics, biomes, water, or space? Explain your answer.

UNIT 1

TEST ANSWERS

Matching

1. Answer: c Objective: 18

2. Answer: d Objective: 14

3. Answer: a Objective: 17

4. Answer: e Objective: 14

5. Answer: f Objective: 17

6. Answer: g Objective: 14

7. Answer: j Objective: 16

8. Answer: i Objective: 18

9. Answer: l Objective: 12

10. Answer: k Objective: 11

Multiple Choice

11. Answer: b Objective: 13

12. Answer: a Objective: 15

13. Answer: a Objective: 18

14. Answer: b Objective: 17

15. Answer: c Objective: 11

16. Answer: b Objective: 18

17. Answer: d Objective: 11

18. Answer: a Objective: 18

19. Answer: d Objective: 14

20. Answer: c Objective: 11

Short Answer

21. Answer:
Energy is moved between the tropics and the polar areas via ocean currents and wind. Both ocean currents and winds are created by differences in air pressure.

Objective: 14

22. Answer:

The Five Themes of Geography are location, place, region, movement, and human-environment interaction. They are useful because they help geographers organize ideas about the world and its people.

Objective: 11

Critical Thinking

23. Answer:

Possible answer: Physical geography affects how the basic needs for daily living are met. The kind of food, clothing, and shelter available to people depends on the land, climate, and resources of the region in which they live. Soil and climate conditions determine what crops can be grown and what other food sources might be available. Clothing and housing are partly determined by the climate conditions as well.

The location and accessibility of a region determines how easily goods that cannot be produced locally can be acquired from other regions. Landforms, such as deserts and mountains, will have a significant impact on ways of life. Some mountain regions may lie at plate boundaries and thus be at risk for earthquakes and volcanic eruptions.

In mountain regions, more people will probably live on the windward side of the mountains, since these areas receive the most moisture from the orographic effect. Water has a tremendous influence on where and how people live. It is essential for human life and is a necessary element of agriculture and industry. Oceans, rivers, and lakes provide a crucial transportation network.

Objective: 18

24. Answer:

Possible answer: Since the oceans supply most of the water that enters the atmosphere, fewer oceans would cause a reduction in the amount of precipitation. The groundwater supply would also be reduced. Without the moderating effect of the ocean, more areas on the earth would experience extremes in temperature.

Objective: 16

25. Answer:

Answers will vary. Students should give clear reasons why they prefer a certain topic. For instance, some students might want to work on forest conservation and thus would be most interested in researching biomes. Other students might want to help drought-stricken areas develop irrigation systems and thus would be most interested in water.

Objective: 11

CHAPTER 7

TEST QUESTIONS

Matching

Match the term with its correct description. One term is not used.

a. acculturation
b. totalitarian
c. ethnic group
d. democratic
e. domestication
f. culture trait

1. A population that shares a common cultural background

2. An activity or behavior repeatedly practiced by people in a society

3. The development of agriculture and the taming of animals

4. The process whereby cultures change as a result of their interactions with each other

5. A type of government in which one person and a few advisors make all the decisions for everyone

Match the term with its correct description. One term is not used.

g. diffusion
h. fundamentalism
i. nationalism
j. innovation
k. culture
l. urbanization

6. Feelings of pride and loyalty for one's country

7. The spreading of ideas to new culture regions, which then adopt these ideas

8. Growth in the proportion of people living in towns and cities

9. A new idea that is accepted into a culture

10. A movement that stresses the importance of following basic traditional principles

Multiple Choice

Circle the letter of the best answer.

11. A culture region is
    a. all of a society's shared values, beliefs, institutions, and technologies.
    b. an activity or behavior repeatedly practiced by people in a society.
    c. an area with many shared culture traits.
    d. a group of people with different cultural backgrounds.

12. All of the following are examples of culture traits except
    a. forms of recreation.   b. wedding rituals.
    c. natural resources.   d. cooking methods.

13. The development of agriculture meant that
    a. people could stay in one place and live in larger groups.
    b. food was more difficult to acquire.
    c. people had to spend more time hunting and gathering.
    d. food became less expensive.

14. Ancient Mesopotamia is considered to be a culture hearth because it is where
    a. the innovation of writing developed.
    b. commercial agriculture originated.
    c. the world's first communications networks flourished.
    d. the Industrial Revolution began.

15. One country's invasion of another to obtain new oil deposits is an example of a conflict caused by
    a. nationalism.   b. fundamentalism.
    c. inequality of resources.   d. differences in values.

16. One result of the changes brought on by the information age is that
    a. new jobs are being created in raw materials industries.
    b. jobs in traditional industries are disappearing.
    c. education has become less important.
    d. totalitarian governments are more widespread.

17. A new classmate, who has recently moved from another state, roller-skates to school every day. The students in the new school think it is a great idea and decide to skate to school too. This might be the start of a cultural process called
    a. innovation.   b. diffusion.
    c. industrialization.   d. domestication.

18. Countries sometimes establish tariffs and quotas to
    a. protect their industries from foreign competition by regulating imports and exports.
    b. encourage more tolerance among religious and ethnic groups.
    c. promote industrialization in foreign countries.
    d. limit the diffusion of culture from one region to another.

19. Two major causes of conflicts between nations or cultures are
    a. culture hearths and fundamentalism.
    b. competition and industrialization.
    c. nationalism and disputes about religion.
    d. tariffs and commercial agriculture.

20. English is one of the most widely spoken languages in the world today. This is a result of
    a. urbanization.   b. fundamentalism.
    c. ethnic groups.   d. diffusion.

Short Answer

Answer the questions in the space provided.

21. Briefly describe the difference between subsistence agriculture and commercial agriculture.
    _____
    _____
    _____
    _____
    _____

22. What is a culture region? Is every country a single culture region? Explain.

_____
_____
_____
_____
_____

Critical Thinking

Write your answers on a separate sheet of paper.

23. How do nationalism, religion, value differences, politics, and the uneven distribution of resources cause conflicts among countries and culture groups?

24. Could industrialization have happened without urbanization? Why or why not?

25. What are the advantages and disadvantages of widespread, instant global communication?

CHAPTER 7

TEST ANSWERS

Matching

1. Answer: c Objective: 11

2. Answer: f Objective: 11

3. Answer: e Objective: 21

4. Answer: a Objective: 12

5. Answer: b Objective: 31

6. Answer: i Objective: 31

7. Answer: g Objective: 12

8. Answer: l Objective: 22

9. Answer: j Objective: 12

10. Answer: h Objective: 31

Multiple Choice

11. Answer: c Objective: 12

12. Answer: c Objective: 11

13. Answer: a Objective: 21

14. Answer: a Objective: 22

15. Answer: c Objective: 31

16. Answer: b Objective: 32

17. Answer: b Objective: 12

18. Answer: a Objective: 31

19. Answer: c Objective: 31

20. Answer: d Objective: 12

Short Answer

21. Answer:
    In subsistence agriculture, people grow food mostly for their own families on small farms. In commercial agriculture, crops are grown for sale on large farms using modern technology.
    Objective: 21

22. Answer:
A culture region is an area with many shared culture traits. Countries and culture regions are not necessarily the same. For example, a culture region can be made up of more than one country. Also, some countries contain several culture regions.

Objective: 12

Critical Thinking

23. Answer:
Conflict often occurs when one group of people feel that their own culture or country is superior to others; intense feelings of such nationalism can lead to unfairness toward these other groups or even to war. Religious conflict can occur when people of one religion feel theirs is the only true religion. Intolerance of other religions can also lead to unrest and war. Cultures that do not easily adapt to change are likely to experience conflict when they come into contact with innovations. Fundamentalism, a movement that stresses the strict following of basic traditional principles, has been the response of many cultures and countries that have felt threatened by innovations and certain values. Politics is another area where conflict can occur. Totalitarian governments sometimes come into conflict with countries that have different types of governments. Democratic governments frequently experience conflict between competing political parties. Finally, because the world's resources are unevenly distributed, conflicts can arise between countries that have raw materials and industries and those that do not. Conflicts over trading rules, such as tariffs and quotas, can develop as well.

Objective: 31

24. Answer:
Possible answer: Probably not. The number of people moving to cities supplied the large labor force necessary for industrialization. They also provided the large market needed to support the manufacture of different goods. In addition, cities usually were located close to trade routes, which provided the transportation network necessary for industrial innovations to spread.

Objective: 22

25. Answer:
Possible answer: The fact that so many cultures share the same information and are exposed to similar culture traits may eventually lead to the development of one global culture instead of several different cultures, leading to the loss of many rich and unique cultural traditions. Advantages might be in the arenas of politics and economics, where decisions must often be made quickly in order for them to be effective.

Objective: 32

CHAPTER 8

TEST QUESTIONS

Matching

Match the term with its correct description. One term is not used.

a. free enterprise
b. gross national product
c. communism
d. foreign aid
e. infrastructure
f. gross domestic product

1. Loans or gifts of money given to developing countries by developed countries

2. The value of goods and services produced by a country in a year, both inside and outside the country

3. An economic system where prices are determined mostly through competition in which buyers and sellers are able to choose what and when to sell and buy

4. Roads, bridges, water supplies, and other facilities that are necessary to build industries and to move goods

5. The goods and services produced within a country during a year, not including income produced outside that country

Match the term with its correct description. One term is not used.

g. command economy
h. secondary industry
i. demography
j. market economy
k. multinational company
l. literacy

6. A system in which consumers determine what is bought and sold by buying or not buying goods and services

7. A business that has activities in many countries

8. The study of the human population that emphasizes facts and figures

9. The ability to read or write

10. A system in which the government makes decisions about wages, production, and prices

Multiple Choice

Circle the letter of the best answer.

11. Primary economic activities are activities that
    a. make direct use of natural resources.
    b. distribute new products to rural areas.
    c. are located near major urban centers.
    d. are performed by professionals with specialized skills.

12. A grocery store in a major city is an example of a
    a. primary industry.   b. secondary industry.
    c. tertiary industry.   d. quaternary industry.

13. Which of the following countries is probably the most developed?
    a. a country that exports agricultural products and minerals and has a 64 percent literacy rate.
    b. a country that has a poor, mostly rural population, with a 31 percent literacy rate.
    c. a country that has a large urban population, few manufacturing and service industries, and a 50 percent literacy rate.
    d. a country that offers widely available health care, is industrialized, and has a 98 percent literacy rate.

14. All of the following might be examined to measure a country's economic development except
    a. the country's level of industrialization.
    b. the country's gross national product.
    c. the country's cultures.
    d. the country's telecommunications systems.

15. An economic system in which resources, industries, and businesses are owned by private individuals is called
    a. communism.   b. demography.
    c. infrastructure.   d. capitalism.

16. A developing country with limited natural resources might improve its economy by
    a. increasing its birthrate.
    b. expanding education.
    c. reducing its per capita GDP.
    d. changing its economic and political systems every few years.

17. In the first stage of a country's population growth, the
    a. birthrate drops and most children live to adulthood.
    b. birthrate and death rate are high but equal.
    c. number of emigrants equals the number of immigrants.
    d. death rate declines while the birthrate remains high.

18. It is likely that, in the future,
    a. birthrates in developed countries will continue to rise dramatically.
    b. literacy among people in developed countries will sharply decrease.
    c. rapid population growth will continue in developing countries.
    d. developing countries will require less food.

19. All of the following are regions of dense human settlement except
    a. northern Africa.   b. eastern China.
    c. eastern North America.   d. India and Bangladesh.

20. The spread of Acquired Immune Deficiency Syndrome (AIDS)
    a. complicates predictions about future population patterns.
    b. was brought under control in the 1980s.
    c. is limited to certain small world regions.
    d. is likely to cause large population increases.

Short Answer

Answer the questions in the space provided.

21. Why is the rate of population growth a serious problem for developing countries?

_____
_____
_____
_____
_____

22. What is the difference between an emigrant and an immigrant? How can emigrants and immigrants affect the size of a country's population?

_____
_____
_____
_____
_____

Critical Thinking

Write your answers on a separate sheet of paper.

23. Are certain economic systems always linked to certain political systems? Explain.

24. In which category of economic activities--primary, secondary, tertiary, or quaternary--do most of the people in developing countries work? Why do you think this is?

25. Imagine that you live in a developing country. A multinational company with headquarters located on another continent has just announced plans to build factories in your country. How do you react to this? Explain.

CHAPTER 8

TEST ANSWERS

Matching

1. Answer: d Objective: 21

2. Answer: b Objective: 12

3. Answer: a Objective: 22

4. Answer: e Objective: 12

5. Answer: f Objective: 12

6. Answer: j Objective: 22

7. Answer: k Objective: 21

8. Answer: i Objective: 31

9. Answer: l Objective: 12

10. Answer: g Objective: 22

Multiple Choice

11. Answer: a Objective: 11

12. Answer: c Objective: 11

13. Answer: d Objective: 12

14. Answer: c Objective: 12

15. Answer: d Objective: 22

16. Answer: b Objective: 21

17. Answer: b Objective: 31

18. Answer: c Objective: 32

19. Answer: a Objective: 31

20. Answer: a Objective: 32

Short Answer

21. Answer:
    Most of the world's developing countries are experiencing rapid population growth. These countries must figure out how to provide food and education for their growing populations. This is particularly difficult in the countries in which resources are already limited.

    Objective: 32

22. Answer:

An emigrant is someone who moves out of a country, while an immigrant is someone who moves into a country. The population of a country will increase if there are more immigrants than emigrants.

Objective: 31

Critical Thinking

23. Answer:

Possible answer: Free-enterprise systems are often found in countries that are democracies; Communist countries, on the other hand, tend to have command economies. Some countries, however, do not fit these patterns. In India, for example, the government controls much of the economy, but the country is a democracy. Meanwhile in China, free enterprise has increased but the people still have few democratic rights.

Objective: 22

24. Answer:

Most people in developing countries are subsistence farmers, so they work in primary economic activities. Possible reasons might include that developing countries have little industry, so few jobs in secondary economic activities are available. Tertiary economic activities, meanwhile, depend on large markets of people who can afford to pay for the services these industries offer, and these markets do not exist in most developing countries. Similarly, quaternary economic activities are based on telecommunications, literacy, and education in general, all of which tend to be somewhat limited in developing countries.

Objective: 11

25. Answer:

Answers will vary. Some students might express hope that the factories will provide work and improve the local economy. On the other hand, students might be concerned about possible pollution problems. Wages might not be as high as are expected. It is possible that cultures might be changed, possibly in a negative way, by the interaction with foreign business.

Objective: 21

CHAPTER 9

TEST QUESTIONS

Matching

Match the term with its correct description. One term is not used.

a. crop rotation
b. ozone
c. photochemical smog
d. sustained yield use
e. fossil fuel
f. acid rain

1. A gas in the upper atmosphere that filters out dangerous solar radiation

2. Air pollution produced when sunlight and exhaust gases mix

3. A system of raising different plants from one year to the next in order to keep soil fertile

4. An energy source, such as coal, petroleum, or natural gas, believed to have been formed from the remains of prehistoric plants and animals

5. Droplets that form as a result of industrial pollutants combining with water vapor in the atmosphere

Match the term with its correct description. One term is not used.

g. deforestation
h. soil salinization
i. desalinization
j. geothermal energy
k. desertification
l. reforestation

6. The removal of salt from seawater

7. Salt buildup that becomes destructive to crops

8. The clearing of trees in tropical rain forests and other areas

9. Heat, used to generate electricity, that has escaped from the earth's interior

10. A loss of plant cover and soil, often resulting from overgrazing and the removal of trees

Multiple Choice

Circle the letter of the <u>best</u> answer.

11. Which of the following is an example of sustained yield use?
    a. prohibiting all access to forests for long periods of time
    b. planting seeds or young trees in order to renew forests
    c. harvesting acorns from an oak forest without destroying the trees
    d. cutting trees for domestic lumber and export to other countries

12. A long-term consequence of the buildup of carbon dioxide in the lower atmosphere may be
    a. acid rain.   b. global warming.
    c. petrochemical smog.   d. geothermal energy.

13. Contour plowing is used to
    a. make fields level.
    b. conserve the soil by planting soil-enriching crops.
    c. reduce salt buildup in the soil.
    d. prevent runoff from eroding topsoil.

14. Controlling population growth can have
    a. only positive effects.
    b. only negative effects.
    c. no effects at all.
    d. both positive and negative effects.

15. One example of a nonrenewable resource is
    a. forests.   b. coal.
    c. solar energy.   d. water.

16. As a result of the 1986 nuclear accident at Chernobyl,
    a. public support for nuclear power has grown.
    b. the former Soviet Union now relies on solar power.
    c. much of Europe was contaminated with radiation.
    d. most of the United States' nuclear power plants have shut down.

17. Renewable energy sources include
    a. nuclear energy, wind power, and petrochemicals.
    b. desalinization, solar energy, and hydropower.
    c. geothermal energy, fertilizers, and fossil fuels.
    d. hydropower, geothermal energy, and solar energy.

18. Saudi Arabia and the neighboring Persian Gulf countries have the largest reserves of
    a. petroleum.   b. lumber.
    c. geothermal energy.   d. ozone.

19. Some countries have controlled population growth so successfully that
    a. a tremendous strain has been placed on their resources.
    b. the world's population is now evenly distributed.
    c. they are now concerned about low birthrates.
    d. they are now concerned about high death rates.

20. The unequal distribution of resources has often led to
    a. reduced world trade.
    b. lower population growth rates.
    c. conflict over access to these resources.
    d. underpopulation of productive regions.

Short Answer

Answer the questions in the space provided.

21. What are the major causes of deforestation in the tropical rain forests?

    _____
    _____
    _____
    _____
    _____
    _____

22. What are some possible effects of global warming? What steps can people take to prevent global warming?

    _____
    _____
    _____
    _____
    _____
    _____

Critical Thinking

Write your answers on a separate sheet of paper.

23. Explain the difference between nonrenewable and renewable resources, and give examples of each. How can all of these resources be conserved?

24. What are the benefits and disadvantages of nuclear power? Do you think the United States should build more nuclear power plants? Explain.

25. Leaders of some developing countries argue that cutting the rain forests provides jobs and investment income, and that these are more important than the environment in the long run. Environmentalists disagree. Can you suggest a compromise?

CHAPTER 9

TEST ANSWERS

Matching

1.Answer: b Objective: 22

2.Answer: c Objective: 22

3.Answer: a Objective: 11

4.Answer: e Objective: 31

5.Answer: f Objective: 21

6.Answer: i Objective: 21

7.Answer: h Objective: 11

8.Answer: g Objective: 12

9.Answer: j Objective: 33

10.Answer: k Objective: 11

Multiple Choice

11.Answer: c Objective: 12

12.Answer: b Objective: 22

13.Answer: d Objective: 11

14.Answer: d Objective: 41

15.Answer: b Objective: 31

16.Answer: c Objective: 32

17.Answer: d Objective: 33

18.Answer: a Objective: 31

19.Answer: c Objective: 41

20.Answer: c Objective: 42

Short Answer

21.Answer:
The major causes of deforestation in the tropical rain forests include the cutting of trees for fuel, the logging of tropical hardwoods, and the clearing of trees for farmland.

Objective: 12

22.Answer:
Possible effects include a rise in sea levels, the dying of some types of vegetation, and the destruction of entire ecosystems. Decreasing the burning of polluting fuels and ending the clearing of forests might guard against global warming.

Objective: 22

Critical Thinking

23.Answer:
Nonrenewable resources, such as fossil fuels and minerals, are either replaced at extremely slow rates by natural processes or not replaced at all. Renewable resources, such as solar energy, soil, water, and forests, can be replaced by natural processes. Careless use, however, can make even renewable resources scarce. Nonrenewable resources can be conserved by careful use and by the development and widespread use of renewable energy resources such as water, solar, wind, and geothermal energy. The earth's resources of soil, water, air, and forests, while renewable, still must be protected. Soil can be conserved by contour plowing, terracing, and crop rotation. Forests can be conserved by reforestation and sustained yield use. Water conservation must be practiced as more people compete for a smaller supply of clean water. Air quality can be protected by clean air laws, modern technology, and the outlawing of chemicals such as CFCs that damage the ozone layer.

Objective: 33

24.Answer:
Possible answer: Nuclear power has been seen as a clean, inexpensive source of power. But disadvantages include the possibility of dangerous accidents and the difficulty of disposing of nuclear waste. Students should support their answers regarding whether or not the United States should build more nuclear power plants.

Objective: 32

25.Answer:
Possible answer: Limited logging and clearing could take place without widespread damage. Trees could be replanted. Sustained yield use could take place in certain portions of the rain forest declared off limits to development.

Objective: 12

UNIT 2

TEST QUESTIONS

Matching

Match the term with its correct description. One term is not used.

a. fossil fuel
b. communism
c. capitalism
d. quota
e. desertification
f. culture

1. An economic system in which resources, industries, and businesses are owned by private individuals

2. A loss of plant and soil cover often caused by overgrazing and the removal of trees

3. All the shared values, beliefs, institutions, and technologies of a society

4. A limit on the amount of a particular good that can be imported into a country

5. An economic and political system in which the government owns or controls the means of production

Match the term with its correct description. One term is not used.

g. telecommunications
h. culture hearth
i. reforestation
j. sustained yield use
k. multinational company
l. culture region

6. An area with many shared culture traits

7. A method by which products can be taken from a forest without damaging the trees

8. A business that has activities in many countries

9. The electronic transmission of information

10. An area where important innovations are developed

Multiple Choice

Circle the letter of the best answer.

11. Before agriculture developed, most people lived by
    a. domesticating animals.
    c. contour plowing.
    b. hunting and gathering.
    d. logging and clearcutting.

12. A country is concerned about competition from foreign industry. It might
    a. insist that domestic industries lower the prices of their goods.
    b. establish tariffs and quotas to regulate imports and exports.
    c. assist developing countries that wish to industrialize.
    d. encourage other countries to elect totalitarian governments.

13. Acculturation is experienced by cultures when they
    a. elect democratic governments and institute market economies.
    b. domesticate plants and animals.
    c. return to traditional farming practices.
    d. change as a result of their interactions with each other.

14. A fairly clean but nonrenewable source of energy is
    a. coal.   b. natural gas.
    c. wind power.   d. geothermal energy.

15. People rely on desalinization plants and wells to
    a. transport water long distances across deserts and mountains.
    b. treat polluted water so that it can be used by urban populations.
    c. provide water in areas where fresh surface waters are limited.
    d. return nutrients to the soil.

16. One aspect of the information age is that
    a. certain fuels, such as oil and coal, are becoming more crucial.
    b. new jobs are being created in traditional industries.
    c. our definition of what materials are valuable is changing.
    d. it now takes more time for information to travel long distances.

17. A problem experienced by many developing countries is
    a. rapid population growth.
    b. a high literacy rate.
    c. economic innovations.
    d. declining birthrates.

18. Factors that may contribute to global warming are
    a. droughts, floods, and earthquakes.
    b. forest fires, volcanic activity, and burning fossil fuels.
    c. soil salinization, crop rotation, and desalinization.
    d. reforestation, solar energy, and silver mining.

19. One cause of world conflict is that most of the earth's natural resources and population
    are
    a. not evenly distributed.   b. regulated by tariffs and quotas.
    c. increasing rapidly.   d. found in Communist countries.

20. Renewable resources can best be defined as those that
    a. can only be replaced by human efforts.
    b. experience sustained yield use.
    c. are restored in deforested tropical regions.
    d. can be replenished by the earth's natural processes.

Short Answer

Answer the questions in the space provided.

21. What are some of the ways by which cultures change?

    _____
    _____
    _____
    _____
    _____

22. What effect did the domestication of plants and animals have on peoples' ways of life?

_____
_____
_____
_____
_____

Critical Thinking

Write your answers on a separate sheet of paper.

23. Describe the relationship between economic development and population. What do you think global population patterns might be like 50 years from now? Explain.

24. Do you think major environmental problems, such as air and water pollution, can be solved? If not, why not? If so, how?

25. What benefits might be brought about by increased industrialization in developing countries? What problems might be created?

UNIT 2

TEST ANSWERS

Matching

1.Answer: c Objective: 24

2.Answer: e Objective: 22

3.Answer: f Objective: 21

4.Answer: d Objective: 21

5.Answer: b Objective: 24

6.Answer: l Objective: 21

7.Answer: j Objective: 22

8.Answer: k Objective: 24

9.Answer: g Objective: 23

10.Answer: h Objective: 21

Multiple Choice

11.Answer: b Objective: 22

12.Answer: b Objective: 24

13.Answer: d Objective: 21

14.Answer: b Objective: 26

15.Answer: c Objective: 27

16.Answer: c Objective: 23

17.Answer: a Objective: 25

18.Answer: b Objective: 28

19.Answer: a Objective: 27

20.Answer: d Objective: 26

Short Answer

21.Answer:
Cultures change when new ideas, or innovations, bring about new ways of doing or thinking about things. Cultures also change when traits from other cultures spread, or diffuse, from region to region.
When cultures change through meeting each other directly, the process is called acculturation.

Objective: 21

22. Answer:
With a reliable source of food, people no longer had to lead a nomadic lifestyle, moving with the seasons in search of food. As a result, they began to live in larger groups, and eventually in towns and cities, where innovations could be shared. People also began to have time to work at things other than food production.

Objective: 22

Critical Thinking

23. Answer:
Possible answer: Economic development is closely related to population. The early development of cities from an agricultural base allowed innovations and technology to spread. Industrialization during the Industrial Revolution was closely tied to growing populations, mostly in urban areas. Today, the world's wealthiest countries are the most industrialized. They have stable populations with a birthrate sometimes lower than the death rate.

In contrast, most of the world's developing countries are experiencing rapid population growth. This rapid growth presents an economic challenge because resources are already limited. Many people in these countries are subsistence farmers or live in poverty in overcrowded cities. It is difficult for them to find employment or to receive quality health care and education. It is likely that population will continue to grow in developing countries, where the birthrate exceeds the death rate.

In 50 years, regions with a harsh climate, where farming is difficult, will probably continue to be lightly populated. Regions where farming is productive and where industrialization might occur are likely to be more populated.

Objective: 25

24. Answer:
Answers will vary. Students should give specific examples to support their arguments. They should refer to specific information in the unit, such as global warming, deforestation, salinization, acid rain, and so on. They might cite examples of environmental preservation techniques such as crop rotation, reforestation, and sustained yield use. They might also discuss the use of renewable energy sources instead of fossil fuels.

Objective: 26

25. Answer:
Possible answer: Increased industrialization might improve a developing country's standard of living by introducing new products and ideas and by providing jobs. The innovations might conflict with traditional ways of life, however. Improved educational systems might create a greater awareness of government and global issues, but this awareness could bring about political conflict over the type of government that should rule and the role the country should play in world affairs. Industrialization also might create an unequal distribution of wealth, causing conflict among the people. Other problems caused by industrialization might be pollution and the depletion of natural resources.

Objective: 24

CHAPTER 10

TEST QUESTIONS

Matching

Match the term with its correct description. One term is not used.

a. piedmont
b. trade deficit
c. plantation
d. mass production
e. edge city
f. basin

1. A low area of land, generally surrounded by mountains

2. A large farm that concentrates on one major crop

3. A situation that occurs when the value of a nation's imports exceeds that of its exports

4. A suburb with many commercial centers

5. An area at or near the foot of a mountain region

Match the term with its correct description. One term is not used.

g. seaboard
h. Sunbelt
i. contiguous
j. Fall Line
k. ghetto
l. Gulf Stream

6. A land area near the ocean

7. The border along which the Piedmont meets the Coastal Plain

8. Bordering each other as a single unit, like states

9. A place in a city where minority groups are concentrated because of economic pressure and social discrimination

10. A warm ocean current that moves tropical water northward

Multiple Choice

Circle the letter of the <u>best</u> answer.

11. The United States is able to feed itself and export food largely because
    a. most of its forests have been cut down for farmland.
    b. more than 20 percent of Americans are farmers.
    c. the nation produces large quantities of oil and coal.
    d. the nation has a wide variety of climates and rich soils.

12. According to the theory of plate tectonics, the Appalachian Mountains were formed when
    a. earthquakes occurred in the Piedmont region.
    b. the Coastal Plain was formed.
    c. eastern North America collided with Africa.
    d. glaciers covered North America during the last ice age.

13. The Interior Plains region of the United States is located
    a. along the Atlantic Ocean and the Gulf of Mexico.
    b. between the Coastal Plain and the Appalachian Mountains.
    c. between the Appalachians and the Rocky Mountains.
    d. between the Rocky Mountains and the Pacific Coast.

14. The earliest inhabitants of North America were
    a. Viking explorers from Europe.
    b. British colonists who settled the Atlantic seaboard.
    c. Native Americans who arrived from Asia.
    d. immigrants from Africa and South America.

15. The climate type dominating the southeastern quarter of the United States is
    a. humid subtropical.   b. highland.
    c. humid continental.   d. desert.

16. One of the major challenges facing the U.S. economy today is how to
    a. respond to competition from Asian and European nations.
    b. encourage industrial research in plastics and steel.
    c. import more from foreign trading partners.
    d. develop the nation's scarce mineral resources.

17. Hawaii is unique among U.S. states because it
    a. is contiguous with Alaska and the Pacific Coast states.
    b. has tropical climates.
    c. has the largest population of any state.
    d. is where North America's lowest point is located.

18. Recent immigration to the United States has mostly been from
    a. Western Europe and Canada.
    b. Africa and Australia.
    c. Middle and South America and Asia.
    d. Russia and Eastern Europe.

19. As the United States has become less industrial and more technological, people have moved
    a. from northern states to southern and western states.
    b. from southeastern states to central states.
    c. from the Great Plains to the Interior Plains.
    d. from the Intermountain region to the Piedmont and the Coastal Plain.

20. The United States was the first country to develop
    a. trade deficits.   b. mass production.
    c. free enterprise.   d. inland water routes.

Short Answer

Answer the questions in the space provided.

21. What is the Coastal Plain, and where is it located?

    _____
    _____
    _____
    _____
    _____

22. Identify three major factors that made the United States a world leader.

_____

_____

_____

_____

_____

Critical Thinking

Write your answers on a separate sheet of paper.

23. If you could choose to live any place in the United States, what region would you choose? Why? In your answer, include a discussion of the landforms, climate types, employment opportunities, and population density in that region.

24. Why do you think the United States attracts so many immigrants from other countries?

25. Urban decay is one of the many challenges facing the United States today. What solutions to the problem can you propose?

CHAPTER 10

TEST ANSWERS

Matching

1. Answer: f Objective: 11

2. Answer: c Objective: 21

3. Answer: b Objective: 32

4. Answer: e Objective: 22

5. Answer: a Objective: 11

6. Answer: g Objective: 11

7. Answer: j Objective: 11

8. Answer: i Objective: 11

9. Answer: k Objective: 22

10. Answer: l Objective: 12

Multiple Choice

11. Answer: d Objective: 31

12. Answer: c Objective: 11

13. Answer: c Objective: 11

14. Answer: c Objective: 21

15. Answer: a Objective: 12

16. Answer: a Objective: 32

17. Answer: b Objective: 12

18. Answer: c Objective: 21

19. Answer: a Objective: 22

20. Answer: b Objective: 31

Short Answer

21. Answer:
    The Coastal Plain is a low region close to sea level that stretches from New York to the Mexican border along the Atlantic Ocean and the Gulf of Mexico.
    Objective: 11

22.Answer:
Possible answers include rich natural resources (including farmland, forests, coal, and oil), a productive population, inland water routes and a strong infrastructure, and free enterprise.

Objective: 31

Critical Thinking

23.Answer:
Answers will vary. Students should support their answers by giving examples of landforms, climates, employment opportunities, and population density. For instance, some students might say that they would like to live in southern California because of its long, sunny summers and mild winters.

Objective: 22

24.Answer:
Possible answer: The United States is a wealthy country where many people have a high standard of living. The government is stable, and people are free to worship and live their lives as they choose without fear of persecution. Many people are attracted by these characteristics. Many also immigrate to the United States to join family members already living here.

Objective: 21

25.Answer:
Answers will vary. Some students may say that rebuilding the inner cities requires both money and commitment, both from those who have abandoned these areas for the suburbs and from those who still live in them. Money can be raised through higher taxes or by stimulating business growth. Crime and drug problems might be countered by providing better schools and jobs.

Objective: 32

CHAPTER 11

TEST QUESTIONS

Matching

Match the term with its correct description. One term is not used.

a. anthracite
b. granite
c. second-growth forest
d. textile
e. break-of-bulk center
f. moraine

1. A speckled, hard, crystalline rock formed deep in the earth's crust

2. A cloth product

3. Trees that cover an area after its original trees have been cut down

4. A ridge of rocks, gravel and sand deposited along the margins of a glacier or ice sheet

5. A hard, high-grade coal

Match the term with its correct description. One term is not used.

g. bituminous
h. peninsula
i. biotechnology
j. Megalopolis
k. borough
l. coke

6. A giant urban region extending along the eastern U.S. seaboard

7. A material used in blast furnaces to purify iron ore for making steel

8. A landform that is surrounded by water on three sides

9. The application of biology to industrial processes

10. An administrative unit of a city, such as New York City

Multiple Choice

Circle the letter of the <u>best</u> answer.

11. A truck farm is a
    a. farm on which crops are raised for purchase in nearby cities.
    b. place where farm machinery and trucks are assembled.
    c. plantation from which trucks carry products to the Midwest.
    d. farm on which trucks are used for all farming chores.

12. In the summer, the climate of the Middle Atlantic states is
    a. cool and humid.   b. warm and dry.
    c. cool and dry.   d. hot and humid.

13. Agriculture in New England is limited because
    a. most of the available farmland has been settled.
    b. the economy centers on tourism and industry.
    c. the area's terrain is rocky and its growing season is short.
    d. the region is entirely covered by forests.

14. Bituminous coal differs from anthracite in that it is a
    a. substance used to purify iron ore instead of making steel.
    b. lower-grade coal that is less expensive to mine.
    c. substance that is used to separate coking coal from moraine.
    d. higher-grade coal that is more expensive to mine.

15. One characteristic that Atlantic City, Gettysburg, and Niagara Falls have in common is that
    they
    a. are all tourist attractions of the Middle Atlantic region.
    b. all belong to the Megalopolis of the Atlantic seaboard.
    c. are all former agricultural areas that have been industrialized.
    d. are all located in the state of New York.

16. The largest and most productive estuary on the Atlantic coast is
    a. the Susquehanna River.   b. Cape Cod.
    c. Chesapeake Bay.   d. Boston Harbor.

17. New England's many colleges and universities have
    a. financed most of the region's oil exploration.
    b. helped the region become a leader in high technology.
    c. been popular tourist destinations.
    d. supported the region's mining industry.

18. The original growth of much of Megalopolis was a result of
    a. migration from the Sunbelt states.
    b. the nodal cities' good port sites.
    c. climate and weather patterns.
    d. the nearness to Washington, D.C.

19. A major problem experienced in Megalopolis is
    a. air and water pollution.
    b. periodic floods and droughts.
    c. building structures that can withstand earthquake damage.
    d. filling newly-created factory jobs.

20. New York City is considered a break-of-bulk center because
    a. its neighborhoods are connected by several toll roads and interstate highways.
    b. shipments of goods are moved from one mode of transportation to another in the city.
    c. it is the commercial and financial center of the United States.
    d. its access to the Atlantic Ocean through the Delaware Bay lowers prices on goods.

Short Answer

Answer the questions in the space provided.

21. What are the major natural resources of the Middle Atlantic region?
    _____
    _____
    _____
    _____
    _____

22. What challenges does New England face?

_____
_____
_____
_____
_____
_____

Critical Thinking

Write your answers on a separate sheet of paper.

23. What are the five major cities of the Northeastern United States, and what characteristics make them important?

24. How do you think the northeastern region—in particular, Megalopolis—can recover from the effects of a continuing industrial decline?

25. If you were involved in the New England fishing industry, how might you react to coastal development in the region?

CHAPTER 11

TEST ANSWERS

Matching

    1.Answer: b Objective: 11

    2.Answer: d Objective: 12

    3.Answer: c Objective: 12

    4.Answer: f Objective: 11

    5.Answer: a Objective: 22

    6.Answer: j Objective: 31

    7.Answer: l Objective: 22

    8.Answer: h Objective: 11

    9.Answer: i Objective: 12

    10.Answer: k Objective: 31

Multiple Choice

    11.Answer: a Objective: 22

    12.Answer: d Objective: 21

    13.Answer: c Objective: 11

    14.Answer: b Objective: 22

    15.Answer: a Objective: 22

    16.Answer: c Objective: 21

    17.Answer: b Objective: 12

    18.Answer: b Objective: 31

    19.Answer: a Objective: 32

    20.Answer: b Objective: 31

Short Answer

    21.Answer:
      Major resources include coal (both bituminous and anthracite), and forest and wilderness areas that serve as wildlife reserves and recreation areas.

      Objective: 22

22.Answer:
Challenges facing the region include acid rain and other forms of pollution, increased industrialization and urbanization, and strains on resources.

Objective: 12

Critical Thinking

23.Answer:
The five major cities of the northeastern region, known as Megalopolis, are New York City, Boston, Philadelphia, Baltimore, and Washington, D.C. Possible answers to the second part: New York City is the location of the headquarters of the United Nations. The city is also an important commercial and financial center and the heart of the nation's garment and fashion industries. It is also an important entertainment and cultural center. In addition, much of the nation's air, rail, and sea traffic passes through New York City.

Boston is New England's largest industrial, educational, financial, and commercial center. Many high-tech businesses are located in and around the city. Philadelphia, another port city, is an important manufacturing, banking, and educational center. In 1776, the Declaration of Independence was signed in Philadelphia. Baltimore, a port city on Chesapeake Bay, is an important industrial urban area. Washington, D.C., meanwhile, is the seat of the nation's government. Many historical sites, monuments, and museums can be found in Washington, D.C.

Objective: 31

24.Answer:
Possible answer: Renovating old, inefficient factories might be one avenue to recovery. Small communities that have depended on one traditional industry may have to broaden their economies to attract workers who might otherwise leave the region. Some students might suggest that encouraging the growth of high-tech industries could help the region.

Objective: 32

25.Answer:
Answers will vary. A person in the fishing industry might be pleased about the prospects for added income, but might also be concerned about the effects of development—especially water pollution—on the region's fishing grounds.

Objective: 12

CHAPTER 12

TEST QUESTIONS

Matching

Match the term with its correct description. One term is not used.

a. diversify
b. Everglades
c. levee
d. Cumberland Plateau
e. Coastal Plain
f. lock

1. A ridge of earth along a riverbank designed to prevent flooding

2. To produce a variety of goods, such as crops, rather than just one

3. The dominant landform of the Southern United States

4. An environmentally damaged wetlands region in Florida

5. A part of a waterway enclosed by gates at each end, used to raise or lower boats as they pass from one water level to another

Match the term with its correct description. One term is not used.

g. bayou
h. tenant farmer
i. New Orleans
j. bilingual
k. barrier island
l. Atlanta

6. A small, sluggish stream that cuts through a delta

7. A long, narrow, sandy landform separated from the mainland by a shallow lagoon or wetland

8. A major oil-tanker port on the Mississippi River

9. Someone who rents land on which to grow crops

10. Having the ability to speak two languages

Multiple Choice

Circle the letter of the best answer.

11. Most of the southern region has a
    a. humid-continental climate.   b. highland climate.
    c. humid-subtropical climate.   d. tropical climate.

12. All of the Florida peninsula is part of the
   a. Piedmont.
   b. Coastal Plain.
   c. Ozark Highlands.
   d. Interior Plains.

13. If you were living in the Southern United States, you would not expect to experience
   a. frequent blizzards.
   b. hurricanes.
   c. severe thunderstorms.
   d. occasional freezes.

14. Major crops grown on farms in the southern states include
   a. lettuce and tomatoes.
   b. citrus fruits and tobacco.
   c. grapes and potatoes.
   d. apples and wheat.

15. The river that forms the international boundary between the United States and Mexico is the
   a. Rio Grande.
   b. Mississippi River.
   c. Arkansas River.
   d. Red River.

16. New Orleans and Houston are both
   a. former Spanish settlements.
   b. major port cities.
   c. located on the Mississippi River.
   d. former cattle-marketing centers.

17. The Southern United States contains about 90 percent of the country's
   a. automobile industry.
   b. tourist industry.
   c. textile industry.
   d. lumber industry.

18. The economies of Texas and Louisiana experience "boom and bust" periods as a result of
   a. shifting prices in the oil and gas industries.
   b. increased demand for timber from regrowth forests.
   c. taxes on sulphur and phosphate mines.
   d. strikes by workers in the textile industry.

19. A city that was established by the Spanish in 1718 and today is bilingual is
   a. Houston, Texas.
   b. New Orleans, Louisiana.
   c. Miami, Florida.
   d. San Antonio, Texas.

20. The sediment carried by the Mississippi River and deposited at the river's mouth forms the
   a. Okefenokee Swamp.
   b. Mississippi Delta.
   c. Tenn-Tom Waterway.
   d. Tombigbee Delta.

Short Answer

Answer the questions in the space provided.

21. How have river projects helped the economy of the Southern United States?
   _____
   _____
   _____
   _____
   _____

22. In spite of the southern region's economic progress, it still faces several challenges. List four of these challenges.
   _____
   _____
   _____
   _____
   _____

Critical Thinking

Write your answers on a separate sheet of paper.

23. Identify the major natural resources of the southern region and explain their importance to the region's economy.

24. Do you think the population of the southern region will continue to rise? Explain.

25. Why do you think most oil refineries in the Southern United States are located along the coast of the Gulf of Mexico?

CHAPTER 12

TEST ANSWERS

Matching

    1.Answer: c Objective: 13

    2.Answer: a Objective: 21

    3.Answer: e Objective: 11

    4.Answer: b Objective: 32

    5.Answer: f Objective: 13

    6.Answer: g Objective: 13

    7.Answer: k Objective: 11

    8.Answer: i Objective: 31

    9.Answer: h Objective: 21

  10.Answer: j Objective: 31

Multiple Choice

  11.Answer: c Objective: 12

  12.Answer: b Objective: 11

  13.Answer: a Objective: 12

  14.Answer: b Objective: 21

  15.Answer: a Objective: 13

  16.Answer: b Objective: 31

  17.Answer: c Objective: 22

  18.Answer: a Objective: 22

  19.Answer: d Objective: 31

  20.Answer: b Objective: 13

Short Answer

  21.Answer:
    The building of canals, levees, dams, reservoirs, and locks has opened more cities as ports and improved the transportation system of the southern region. River projects also provide hydroelectricity, irrigation water, and flood control.

    Objective: 13

22. Answer:
Students may list four of the following: low literacy rates, low per capita incomes, low health standards, high employment rates, poverty, urban congestion, strained public facilities, ghetto growth, pollution, housing shortages, and environmental damage caused by pollution and new drainage systems.

Objective: 32

Critical Thinking

23. Answer:
The southern states have a variety of natural resources, including marine resources, forests, and mineral resources. Marine resources, including oysters and shrimp, are found in the waters of the Atlantic and the Gulf of Mexico. More than one third of commercial forest production in the United States is generated by the southern states; forests support the paper and pulp industry. Mineral resources in the region are also plentiful. These include coal, sulfur, salt, iron ore, phosphates, oil, and natural gas. Texas and Louisiana produce about one third of the United States's crude oil. The regional economy experiences ups and downs as a result of shifting prices on the world market. Low prices result in high unemployment rates and a loss in government income.

Objective: 22

24. Answer:
Possible answer: It is likely that the region will continue to experience immigration from Middle and South American countries and from other U.S. states, especially those that have experienced industrial decline. Low labor costs, a generally warm climate, good ports and airports, abundant natural resources, and relatively inexpensive land will probably continue to attract people to the region.

Objective: 31

25. Answer:
Possible answer: Much oil production in the region is from offshore oil rigs on the Gulf of Mexico's continental shelf. Also, the various ports on the coast, particularly Houston, ship refined oil to various destinations.

Objective: 22

CHAPTER 13

TEST QUESTIONS

Matching

Match the term with its correct description. One term is not used.

a. tropical savanna
b. St. Lawrence Seaway
c. Corn Belt
d. humid continental
e. Dairy Belt
f. St. Marys River

1. The waterway that connects Lake Superior to lakes Michigan and Huron

2. A region in the Midwest where corn, beef, and pork are produced

3. The climate found throughout the Midwest region

4. A region in the Midwest where products such as milk, butter, and cheese are produced

5. An important waterway that allows large ships to travel from the Atlantic Ocean through eastern Canada to the U.S. Midwest

Match the term with its correct description. One term is not used.

g. dredge
h. interstate highway system
i. Ozark Plateau
j. township and range system
k. channel
l. Mesabi Range

6. To straighten a waterway, such as the major tributaries of the Mississippi River

7. The most rugged landform region of the Midwest states

8. To dig out a waterway, such as the major tributaries of the Mississippi River

9. The only place in the Midwest where iron ore is mined

10. A survey system developed by the federal government in the 1780s to divide and sell land northwest of the Ohio River

Multiple Choice

Circle the letter of the <u>best</u> answer.

11. When the interstate highway system was built,
    a. small towns bypassed by the new highways experienced economic decline.
    b. many people from the Northeast moved onto and settled one-mile square sections of midwestern land.
    c. midwesterners were encouraged to relocate to the Sunbelt states.
    d. many airports across the country were shut down.

12. A recent change in the Midwest is that
    a. the township and range system has taken land away from farmers.
    b. farmers can no longer afford to ship farm products to other states.
    c. the price of oil and natural gas has fallen on the world market.
    d. there are more large, corporate farms and fewer small, family-owned farms.

13. Farmers who rotate their crops
    a. are required to grow soybeans one year and wheat the next.
    b. do not use commercial fertilizers.
    c. substitute crops such as clover and soybeans for corn in some years to keep the soil fertile.
    d. always graze their cattle in unplanted fields.

14. Detroit and St. Louis were both founded as
    a. industrial cities.   b. French fur-trading posts.
    c. financial and retail centers. d. pioneer supply towns.

15. The Midwest's industrial cities once flourished primarily because they
    a. benefited from the region's abundant hydroelectric power.
    b. contained a large number of skilled agricultural workers.
    c. attracted immigrants from India and China.
    d. were located on or near important transportation routes.

16. One advantage of the interstate highway system in the Midwest is that it
    a. makes it faster to drive than fly between certain cities.
    b. has boosted the economies of bypassed towns.
    c. connects the major metropolitan areas of the region.
    d. has completely replaced waterways as the region's major transportation network.

17. The landforms of the northern part of the Midwest
    a. resemble the highland region of the Appalachian Mountains.
    b. contain thousands of lakes left behind by glaciers during the last ice age.
    c. include arid deserts as well as humid-continental steppes.
    d. are mainly steep, rugged mountains and deep valleys.

18. The city that has the world's busiest airport and is the busiest port on the Great Lakes is
    a. Chicago.   b. St. Paul.
    c. Kansas City.   d. Cleveland.

19. A major city on Lake Erie now making a comeback from industrial decline is
    a. Detroit.   b. Minneapolis.
    c. St. Louis.   d. Cleveland.

20. The major landform region to which almost all of the Midwest belongs is the
    a. Coastal Plain.   b. Interior Plains.
    c. Rocky Mountains.   d. Mesabi Range.

Short Answer

Answer the questions in the space provided.

21. Describe the climate of the Midwest region.

_____
_____
_____
_____
_____

22. Why is the Corn Belt also called the Feed and Grain Belt?

_____
_____
_____
_____
_____

Critical Thinking

Write your answers on a separate sheet of paper.

23. Explain the development of the industrial cities of the Midwest region.

24. How, in your opinion, might the economy of the Midwest best be improved?

25. What kinds of problems do you think might be caused when a river is dredged and channeled?

CHAPTER 13

TEST ANSWERS

Matching

   1.Answer: f Objective: 12

   2.Answer: c Objective: 22

   3.Answer: d Objective: 11

   4.Answer: e Objective: 22

   5.Answer: b Objective: 12

   6.Answer: k Objective: 12

   7.Answer: i Objective: 11

   8.Answer: g Objective: 12

   9.Answer: l Objective: 31

 10.Answer: j Objective: 21

Multiple Choice

 11.Answer: a Objective: 41

 12.Answer: d Objective: 21

 13.Answer: c Objective: 21

 14.Answer: b Objective: 42

 15.Answer: d Objective: 31

 16.Answer: c Objective: 41

 17.Answer: b Objective: 11

 18.Answer: a Objective: 42

 19.Answer: d Objective: 42

 20.Answer: b Objective: 11

Short Answer

21.Answer:
All of the Midwest region has a humid-continental climate with four distinct seasons. In general, the southern part of the region experiences warmer summers and milder winters than the northern part, but the entire region is subject to cold arctic air and snow in winter. Rainfall is usually plentiful, and thunderstorms and tornadoes are common.

Objective: 11

22.Answer:
The Corn Belt is also called the Feed and Grain Belt because most of the corn grown in the region is used to feed livestock. Farmers feed the corn to beef cattle and hogs to fatten them before they are sent to market.

Objective: 22

Critical Thinking

23.Answer:
Early settlements in the Midwest were based in part on their locations on or near important transportation routes. Several industrial cities in the Midwest region began as ports on the Great Lakes, where they had access to coal from the Appalachians, Illinois, Indiana, and Ohio. They also had access to iron-ore deposits which were shipped to other industrial cities. Many other industrial cities in the region developed in the Ohio River valley, which extends through southern Illinois, Ohio, and Indiana. The Ohio River connects to the Mississippi River, making trade with other regions of the country possible. Some of the cities in this region are Cincinnati and Evansville.

Objective: 31

24.Answer:
Possible answer: Students should note that industry has always been important to the economy of the Midwest region. They may suggest that all industries follow the lead of the automobile industry, which has refurbished its factories and attracted foreign investment to the region. Students might also suggest increasing the number of high-tech industries in the region. Some students may note that there is a link between economic well-being and environmental quality, and that cleaning up the region's polluted air and water could have a positive economic impact.

Objective: 32

25.Answer:
Possible answer: Dredging a river stirs up mud from the river bottom, upsetting a river's food chain. Channeling a river might lead to flooding and erosion of the river banks, disrupting the river's ecosystem.

Objective: 12

CHAPTER 14

TEST QUESTIONS

Matching

Match the term with its correct description. One term is not used.

a. ghost town
b. badland
c. aqueduct
d. chinook
e. center pivot irrigation
f. shelterbelt

1. A strong mountain wind that affects the western portions of the Great Plains

2. An area that has been eroded into small gullies by wind and water and left without soil and vegetation

3. A row of trees that blocks wind, thereby protecting soil from erosion

4. A type of canal that often carries water long distances from a river or lake to a dry area

5. A formerly prosperous but now deserted community

Match the term with its correct description. One term is not used.

g. tree line
h. Wheat Belt
i. strip mining
j. Continental Divide
k. toponym
l. land reclamation

6. A place-name that often reflects a region's history and culture

7. A process in which large machines take away soil and rocks to reach coal deposits

8. The elevation above which trees cannot grow

9. The border that separates the major river systems of North America into those that flow eastward and those that flow westward

10. A process in which erosion is prevented following mining activity

Multiple Choice

Circle the letter of the best answer.

11. The earliest inhabitants of the Intermountain West region were
    a. Mormons.   b. Native Americans.
    c. Spanish.   d. British.

12. Kansas, North Dakota, and Oklahoma are all located in the
   a. Great Plains.
   b. Intermountain West.
   c. Rocky Mountains.
   d. Columbia Plateau.

13. A major consequence of the Homestead Act of 1862 was that
   a. farmers from the Midwest were encouraged to move to California.
   b. the open plains were divided into fenced ranches and farms.
   c. miners were able to claim all of the profits from their holdings.
   d. buffalo herds became larger.

14. The major source of water for much of Nevada, Arizona, and southern California is the
   a. Colorado River.
   b. Ogallala Aquifer.
   c. Snake River.
   d. Great Salt Lake.

15. Center pivot irrigation makes the shape of fields
   a. square.
   b. rectangular.
   c. triangular.
   d. circular.

16. The dominant climate of the Great Plains region is the
   a. humid-continental climate.
   b. steppe climate.
   c. marine-west-coast climate.
   d. tundra climate.

17. The industry in the Rocky Mountain region that would probably be most seriously affected by widespread strip mining is
   a. banking.
   b. agriculture.
   c. tourism.
   d. high technology.

18. The major landform regions of the Intermountain West region are the Basin and Range region, the Colorado Plateau, and the
   a. Colorado Piedmont.
   b. Grand Tetons.
   c. Sand Hills.
   d. Columbia Plateau.

19. The largest city in the Intermountain West is
   a. Phoenix, Arizona.
   b. Las Vegas, Nevada.
   c. St. Louis, Missouri.
   d. Las Cruces, New Mexico.

20. In the Great Plains region, farmers often combine livestock raising with
   a. cotton farming.
   b. wheat farming.
   c. mining.
   d. rice farming.

Short Answer

Answer the questions in the space provided.

21. Where is the Wheat Belt located? Why is it important?
   _____
   _____
   _____
   _____
   _____
   _____

22. Identify three challenges facing the Great Plains region.
   _____
   _____
   _____
   _____
   _____

Critical Thinking

Write your answers on a separate sheet of paper.

23. Explain the importance of water to the Great Plains and Intermountain West regions. From what sources do these regions get their water?

24. Why do you think there are no major cities in the Rocky Mountains region?

25. Do you think that the population of the Interior West region will increase substantially in the future? Why or why not?

CHAPTER 14

TEST ANSWERS

Matching

1.Answer: d Objective: 11

2.Answer: b Objective: 11

3.Answer: f Objective: 12

4.Answer: c Objective: 31

5.Answer: a Objective: 22

6.Answer: k Objective: 32

7.Answer: i Objective: 12

8.Answer: g Objective: 21

9.Answer: j Objective: 21

10.Answer: l Objective: 12

Multiple Choice

11.Answer: b Objective: 32

12.Answer: a Objective: 11

13.Answer: b Objective: 12

14.Answer: a Objective: 31

15.Answer: d Objective: 13

16.Answer: b Objective: 11

17.Answer: c Objective: 22

18.Answer: d Objective: 31

19.Answer: a Objective: 32

20.Answer: b Objective: 12

Short Answer

21.Answer:
The Wheat Belt is located in North and South Dakota, Montana, Nebraska, Oklahoma, Colorado, and Texas. It is important because wheat is a major U.S. crop both for export and for domestic consumption, and most U.S. wheat is grown in this region.

Objective: 12

22.Answer:
Possible answers include the threat of droughts, dust storms, hailstorms, insects, and plant disease; environmental challenges such as soil erosion and air pollution (particularly in Denver); and international economic factors, such as the price of wheat on world markets.

Objective: 13

Critical Thinking

23.Answer:
Possible answer: Water is a scarce resource in the Great Plains and Intermountain West regions. The Great Plains, which is dominated by a dry steppe climate, receives less than 20 inches (50 cm) of rainfall per year. Water for irrigation is pumped from the Ogallala Aquifer, an underground water source that stretches from South Dakota to Texas. At one point, the water table dropped sharply as a result of increased irrigation and lack of conservation, but the depletion rate has now slowed due to greater efficiency in irrigation. The rivers of the Great Plains, once full in the spring but nearly empty in the summer, are now regulated by major dam-building projects that control the flow of these rivers, making farming less risky. Also, center-pivot irrigation has become a common form of irrigation in the Great Plains.

In the Intermountain West region, too, much agriculture relies on irrigation. The Colorado River, controlled by dams such as Hoover Dam and Glen Canyon Dam, provides most of the southern part of the region's irrigation water. Aqueduct systems carry water to towns and farms hundreds of miles from the Colorado River.

Objective: 13

24.Answer:
Possible answer: The Rocky Mountains' mountainous terrain, limited agriculture, and small population have not encouraged the growth of large cities. Also, tourism is one of the region's most valuable industries. Because this tourism relies mainly on the presence of large scenic and wilderness areas, the destruction of these areas due to the building of cities could have a negative economic impact on the region.

Objective: 22

25.Answer:
Possible answer: Some students may say that population will increase in some areas of the region, such as the Intermountain West, to which people are attracted because of its wide-open spaces and warm, sunny climate. Other students may say that the population of the region will probably not increase significantly, due to the scarcity of water resources.

Objective: 32

CHAPTER 15

TEST QUESTIONS

Matching

Match the term with its correct description. One term is not used.

a. agribusiness
b. marine west coast
c. tundra
d. Central Valley
e. Silicon Valley
f. multicultural region

1. Farming on large modern farms, many of which are owned by large corporations

2. The world's largest center for computer firms, located south of San Francisco

3. The term for an area in which people of many diverse cultures have settled

4. The climate type found in the area along the Arctic Ocean coast of Alaska

5. One of the United States' richest agricultural regions, located in California

Match the term with its correct description. One term is not used.

g. hot spot
h. humid tropical
i. caldera
j. clear-cut
k. Mediterranean
l. panhandle

6. An area where all the trees have been removed

7. A large depression formed in the land's surface after a major eruption and collapse of a volcanic mountain

8. An area where molten material from the earth's interior rises through the crustal plate

9. A narrow arm of land attached to a larger region

10. The climate type in most of coastal southern and central California

Multiple Choice

Circle the letter of the best answer.

11. If you lived on the windward side of the Cascades, you would
    a. be living in a marine-west-coast climate region.
    b. be living just north of Mount McKinley.
    c. probably be living near San Diego or Los Angeles.
    d. be living in a dry area with little rainfall.

12. Before the Europeans arrived, the largest native Alaskan group consisted of the
    a. Russians.
    b. Canadians.
    c. Inuit (Eskimo).
    d. Polynesians.

13. The climate of the eastern, windward side of the Hawaiian islands is
    a. humid tropical.
    b. Mediterranean.
    c. tropical savanna.
    d. humid subtropical.

14. Nearly three fourths of Alaska's land is
    a. used for farming.
    b. owned by the federal government.
    c. located in the Alaskan panhandle.
    d. inhabited solely by the Inuit (Eskimo).

15. The climate found in the interior of Alaska is
    a. subarctic.
    b. marine west coast.
    c. tundra.
    d. humid continental.

16. One of California's most important yet endangered resources is
    a. gold.
    b. natural gas.
    c. water.
    d. fertile soil.

17. Hawaii's economy is dominated by
    a. subsistence farming.
    b. tourism.
    c. high-tech industries.
    d. manufacturing industries.

18. Most of California's current population growth is due to
    a. immigration from Middle and South America and Asia.
    b. increased birthrates among residents.
    c. low death rates among residents.
    d. higher wages and better health care than that of other U.S. states.

19. Hawaii's cost of living is high because
    a. prices for sugarcane and pineapples are high.
    b. tourists are willing to pay high prices for services.
    c. 80 percent of all materials, energy, and food are imported.
    d. everything Hawaiians need is produced on the islands.

20. Fishing and forest resources are probably most important to the economy of
    a. California.
    b. Oregon and Washington.
    c. Nevada and Utah.
    d. Hawaii.

Short Answer

Answer the questions in the space provided.

21. What events have caused Alaska's population to grow since 1867?

    _____
    _____
    _____
    _____
    _____
    _____

22. What are the major cities of Oregon and Washington? What economic activities are important
    in these cities?

    _____
    _____
    _____
    _____
    _____
    _____

Critical Thinking

Write your answers on a separate sheet of paper.

23. What major issues face the residents of California, Oregon, and Washington today?

24. Do you think the federal government should continue to protect the wilderness areas of Alaska, or should it open up these areas for economic development?

25. Identify two characteristics of Hawaii that make it unique among all U.S. states.

CHAPTER 15

TEST ANSWERS

Matching

1. Answer: a Objective: 12

2. Answer: e Objective: 12

3. Answer: f Objective: 12

4. Answer: c Objective: 31

5. Answer: d Objective: 11

6. Answer: j Objective: 22

7. Answer: i Objective: 21

8. Answer: g Objective: 41

9. Answer: l Objective: 31

10. Answer: k Objective: 11

Multiple Choice

11. Answer: a Objective: 21

12. Answer: c Objective: 32

13. Answer: a Objective: 41

14. Answer: b Objective: 32

15. Answer: a Objective: 31

16. Answer: c Objective: 12

17. Answer: b Objective: 42

18. Answer: a Objective: 12

19. Answer: c Objective: 42

20. Answer: b Objective: 22

Short Answer

21. Answer:
The discovery of gold in the late 1800s attracted many new settlers to Alaska. Then after Alaska became a state in 1959, more population growth was spurred by the oil industry.

Objective: 32

22.Answer:
Major cities of Oregon and Washington include Seattle, Tacoma, and Portland. All of these cities, located on the Pacific Rim, are important seaports. Seattle and Portland also are home to a number of high-tech industries.

Objective: 22

Critical Thinking

23.Answer:
Possible answer: The major issues facing these states include preparing for natural disasters, protecting the environment, providing water for industry, agriculture, and personal use, and dealing with rapid population growth. As part of the Pacific Ring of Fire, California is subject to severe earthquakes, and Washington and Oregon experience both earthquakes and volcanic eruptions. Furthermore, issues concerning the environment are very important to the region. For example, conflicts between the lumber industry and environmental groups, particularly in Oregon and Washington, have yet to be resolved. In addition, droughts and the scarcity of water resources remain a major challenge—overuse of groundwater for irrigation has lowered California's water table. Finally, rapid population growth in all of these Pacific Coast states has contributed to problems such as high housing costs, loss of farmland, increased crime, traffic congestion, and air pollution.

Objective: 12

24.Answer:
Answers will vary. Students who think the government should continue to protect the wilderness areas may argue that the land should be preserved for the sake of its beauty, for the protection of wildlife and ecosystems in general, and for tourism. Others may argue that if these areas were made available for development, unemployment in the state might no longer be a serious problem and the cost of living might fall.

Objective: 31

25.Answer:
Possible answers include that Hawaii is the only state that consists entirely of islands, the only state with a humid-tropical climate, and the only state in which Asian Americans make up a majority of the population.

Objective: 41

CHAPTER 16

TEST QUESTIONS

Matching

Match the term with its correct description. One term is not used.

a. regionalism
b. dominion
c. muskeg
d. Grand Banks
e. Canadian Shield
f. parliament

1. A territory or sphere of influence

2. A forested swamp that melts only during the summer

3. A semicircular band of rocky uplands and plateaus surrounding Hudson Bay

4. The political and emotional support for one's state or province before support for one's country

5. A lawmaking body

Match the term with its correct description. One term is not used.

g. portage
h. province
i. hinterland
j. potash
k. newsprint
l. deport

6. An inexpensive paper used mainly for newspapers

7. A low land area across which boats and their cargoes can be carried

8. A mineral that is an important raw material in the manufacturing of fertilizers

9. A region beyond the center of a country or city

10. To send out of a country

Multiple Choice

Circle the letter of the best answer.

11. Regionalism has flourished in Canada because of all of the following factors except
    a. economic interdependence among the provinces.
    b. political inequalities among the provinces in the ways Canada is governed.
    c. differences of language and culture among and within some provinces.
    d. long distances and physical barriers that isolate some provinces.

12. More than half of Canada's electric power comes from
    a. nuclear power plants.   b. hydroelectric plants.
    c. coal-powered plants.   d. solar-powered plants.

13. Only about 80,000 people live in all of
    a. the Maritime Provinces.
    b. Quebec and Ontario.
    c. British Columbia and Saskatchewan.
    d. the Northwest Territories, the Yukon, and Nunavut.

14. Alberta's major natural resource, on which all of Canada depends, is
    a. oil.   b. potash.   c. fish.   d. coal.

15. An issue that has threatened to break up Canada for years is whether
    a. explorers should drill for oil in northern Canada.
    b. British Columbia should join with Ontario.
    c. Quebec should become an independent country.
    d. Canada should continue to trade with the United States.

16. The first of the following events to take place was
    a. the passage of the British North America Act by the British Parliament.
    b. the establishment of French farms along the St. Lawrence River and in Nova Scotia.
    c. the British capture of Quebec in a war with France.
    d. the division of Canada into Upper Canada and Lower Canada.

17. Farming is limited in the Maritime Provinces because
    a. the climate brings snow and freezing temperatures year-round.
    b. farmers are unable to afford expensive farm machinery.
    c. farmers do not regularly rotate their crops.
    d. the growing season is short and the soil is thin and rocky.

18. Most residents of Quebec
    a. are descended from families in Ontario.
    b. live in the city of Winnipeg.
    c. speak French as their first language.
    d. are employed in government jobs.

19. Canada's Prairie Provinces are
    a. Ontario and Quebec.
    b. British Columbia, Nova Scotia, and Nunavut.
    c. the Yukon and New Brunswick.
    d. Manitoba, Saskatchewan, and Alberta.

20. The climate of eastern and central southern Canada is
    a. marine west coast.   b. tundra.
    c. humid continental.   d. steppe.

Short Answer

Answer the questions in the space provided.

21. List three of Canada's major landform regions.

    _____
    _____
    _____
    _____
    _____

22. What relationships exist between Canada and the United States?

_____
_____
_____
_____
_____

Critical Thinking

Write your answers on a separate sheet of paper.

23. Discuss the regionalism that causes conflicts between the various regions and provinces of Canada. Use specific examples.

24. If you could choose to live in any part of Canada, where would it be? Give specific reasons for your decision.

25. Quebec, with its predominantly French-Canadian culture, has often threatened to separate from the rest of Canada. What would be the advantages and/or disadvantages of such a separation?

CHAPTER 16

TEST ANSWERS

Matching

 1. Answer: b   Objective: 21

 2. Answer: c   Objective: 11

 3. Answer: e   Objective: 11

 4. Answer: a   Objective: 41

 5. Answer: f   Objective: 21

 6. Answer: k   Objective: 12

 7. Answer: g   Objective: 22

 8. Answer: j   Objective: 12

 9. Answer: i   Objective: 31

10. Answer: l   Objective: 22

Multiple Choice

11. Answer: a   Objective: 41

12. Answer: b   Objective: 12

13. Answer: d   Objective: 31

14. Answer: a   Objective: 42

15. Answer: c   Objective: 33

16. Answer: b   Objective: 22

17. Answer: d   Objective: 32

18. Answer: c   Objective: 33

19. Answer: d   Objective: 31

20. Answer: c   Objective: 11

Short Answer

21. Answer:
Students should list three of the following: the Appalachian Mountains, the St. Lawrence Lowlands and Great Lakes, the Interior Plains, the Canadian Shield, the mountains of the Canadian west, and the mountains of the eastern Arctic.

Objective: 11

22. Answer:

Canada and the United States have both economic and cultural relationships. Economically, Canada trades its natural resources for manufactured goods made in the United States, and many Canadian firms do most of their business with U.S. firms. Culturally, the two countries are similar; however, Canadians have been able to maintain their own distinct culture despite the influence of U.S. popular culture.

Objective: 42

Critical Thinking

23. Answer:

Possible answer: Regionalism, the political and emotional support for one's region before one's country, has often threatened to divide Canada into several different countries. Various conflicts exist among the individual provinces and between the provinces and the national government. For example, several provinces share a distrust of the national government in Ottawa. Culture and language have been the source of ongoing conflicts among people in Ontario and Quebec. Alberta, which has enormous tax revenues from petroleum, does not wish to share these revenues with Ottawa. And British Columbia already feels cut off from much of Canada due to its far western location and high mountains.

Objective: 41

24. Answer:

Answers will vary. Students should give specific reasons for their choices, citing the influence of landforms and climate, cultural geography, economic opportunities, and other factors.

Objective: 31

25. Answer:

Answers will vary. Advantages might include the lessening of tensions with Canada's national government over the separation issue as well as the preservation of Quebec's cultural heritage. Disadvantages might be that a newly independent Quebec would separate the eastern provinces from the rest of Canada. The western provinces might then declare their independence as well. Each part of a divided Canada would also have fewer economic resources to draw on than they did as part of a larger country. Economic problems might occur as a result.

Objective: 33

UNIT 3

TEST QUESTIONS

Matching

Match the term with its correct description. One term is not used.
a. Interior Plains
b. land reclamation
c. Megalopolis
d. agribusiness
e. Metroplex
f. Appalachian Mountains

1. An urban region in the Northeastern states that contains some of the largest cities in the United States

2. Farming on large, modern farms, many of which are owned by large corporations

3. A major landform of the eastern United States and Canada

4. A process in which topsoil is retained and restored to prevent erosion after mining

5. A large landform region drained by the Mississippi River and its tributaries

Match the term with its correct description. One term is not used.
g. Toronto
h. steppe
i. Corn Belt
j. Ottawa
k. marine west coast
l. Fall Line

6. The climate of the western parts of the Pacific Northwest states and the southwestern part of British Columbia

7. Canada's capital city, located in the province of Ontario

8. The climate of the Great Plains

9. An important agricultural region in the Midwest

10. The border along which the Coastal Plain meets the Piedmont

Multiple Choice

Circle the letter of the <u>best</u> answer.

11. Canada is not evenly populated because
    a. the rugged coastal regions cannot support large settlements.
    b. few people live in the harsh climate regions of the vast Canadian north.
    c. most Canadians live close to Canada's natural resources, which are mostly in the south.
    d. water resources are scarce in the Canadian north, although food is plentiful.

12. A major challenge for the Northeastern United States is to
   a. convince people to move away from Megalopolis.
   b. protect its vital water sources from pollution.
   c. prepare for earthquakes and other natural disasters.
   d. help residents of edge cities find employment.

13. British Columbia, Oregon, and Washington have all benefited from the natural resource of
   a. petroleum.
   b. fertile soils deposited by glaciers.
   c. coal and iron ore.
   d. extensive forests.

14. The original inhabitants of Hawaii were
   a. Polynesians.   b. Spanish.
   c. Inuit (Eskimo).   d. Japanese.

15. Megalopolis includes
   a. Houston, Miami, and Atlanta.
   b. Washington, D.C., Boston, and Philadelphia.
   c. Salt Lake City, Phoenix, and Denver.
   d. Los Angeles, San Francisco, and Portland.

16. Since 1867, when the Dominion of Canada was created, Canada has had close ties with
   a. Britain.   b. France.   c. Mexico.   d. Germany.

17. The Colorado River
   a. runs from Washington to Indiana.
   b. drains the northern part of the Interior Plains.
   c. drains into the Atlantic Ocean.
   d. is the major source of water for much of the U.S. southwest.

18. Most metropolitan areas in the United States today
   a. are found in the Midwest.
   b. contain large central cities and growing suburbs.
   c. have overcome the problems of discrimination and poverty.
   d. are not linked to each other by highways and railroads.

19. The population of the Intermountain West region
   a. has decreased steadily since World War II.
   b. has grown due to the region's abundant water resources and cool climate.
   c. fell sharply during the 1980s when wheat prices dropped and farms were abandoned.
   d. has recently experienced the nation's most rapid growth.

20. Both U.S. and Canadian farmers are challenged continually by
   a. land limits placed on them by the township and range system.
   b. the pressures of regionalism.
   c. conflicts with their governments.
   d. the uncertainties of the weather and world markets.

Short Answer

Answer the questions in the space provided.

21. What is the Continental Divide?

_____
_____
_____
_____
_____

22. Name three climate types in the United States and Canada that support dense human settlement. For each one, list a region where it is found.

———————————————————————————
———————————————————————————
———————————————————————————
———————————————————————————
———————————————————————————

Critical Thinking

Write your answers on a separate sheet of paper.

23. Describe how landforms, climate, and resources have influenced where and how Americans and Canadians live.

24. If you were a government official in either Canada or the United States, do you think you would be more inclined to support environmental or economic interests? Why? Do you think it would be possible to support both at the same time? If so, how?

25. How are Canadian provinces similar to and different from U.S. states?

UNIT 3

TEST ANSWERS

Matching

1. Answer: c

2. Answer: d

3. Answer: f

4. Answer: b

5. Answer: a

6. Answer: k

7. Answer: j

8. Answer: h

9. Answer: i

10. Answer: l

Multiple Choice

11. Answer: b

12. Answer: b

13. Answer: d

14. Answer: a

15. Answer: b

16. Answer: a

17. Answer: d

18. Answer: b

19. Answer: d

20. Answer: d

Short Answer

21. Answer:
    The Continental Divide, formed by the crest of the Rocky Mountains, divides the major river systems of North America into those that flow eastward and those that flow westward.

22. Answer:
    Possible answers include the humid-continental climate (U.S. Northeast and Midwest, southern Canada), the humid-subtropical climate (southeastern United States), the marine-west-coast climate (northwestern United States, southwestern Canada), and the Mediterranean climate (southern and central California).

Critical Thinking

23. Answer:
    Possible answer: Most Americans live in the Coastal Plain, Piedmont, Appalachians, Interior Plains, and Pacific Coast landform regions, and in the humid-continental, humid-subtropical, marine-west-coast, and Mediterranean climate regions. Americans live in these regions because of abundant natural resources, including water, fertile soil, fish, forests, or mineral resources. The climate in these regions is generally mild enough to support agriculture. Fewer people live in the drier Intermountain and southwestern states, where arid climates and scarce water resources have made settlement more difficult. However, as technology has been developed to carry water greater distances, population in these regions has increased.
    Most Canadians live in the southern part of the country, near the border with the United States. Many people live in the St. Lawrence and Great Lakes Lowlands, which contain some of the most fertile soils in the country and have important waterways that facilitate industry and trade. The climate of northern Canada is very harsh, with a subarctic or tundra climate. Thus, although there are many natural resources in this frozen northern region, the northern provinces are sparsely settled. The climate of the southern regions, where most Canadians live, is either marine west coast, in the southwestern part of British Columbia, or humid continental, in the central and eastern parts of southern Canada. These regions support fishing, agriculture, industry, and other economic activities.

24. Answer:
    Answers will vary. Some students may say that what is good for the environment may ultimately be good for the economy as well. Other students, however, may be more concerned with jobs and short-term profits, even at the expense of the environment. Some students may say that they would try to work out compromises and achieve a balance between the different interests.

25. Answer:
    Both the United States and Canada have strong national governments with semi-independent political units (states in the United States and provinces in Canada). Canadian provinces, however, are much more powerful than U.S. states. Many Canadians identify themselves most closely with their provinces, while most Americans identify themselves more with the nation than with their states. Some Canadians argue that certain provinces, namely Quebec, should separate politically from Canada and become completely independent.

CHAPTER 17

TEST QUESTIONS

Matching

Match the term with its correct description. One term is not used.

a. labor intensive
b. cacao
c. indigenous
d. shantytown
e. hacienda
f. indigo

1. Native to a region

2. A plant used to make a blue dye

3. A small tree that produces the bean used to make chocolate

4. Requiring a large work force

5. A large estate where peasants work the landowner's land in addition to growing their own crops

Match the term with its correct description. One term is not used.

g. mestizos
h. llanos
i. mulattos
j. land reform
k. isthmus
l. pampas

6. A narrow neck of land that acts as a bridge between two larger bodies of land

7. People with both Native American and European ancestors

8. Large plains, formed by erosion over millions of years, in Colombia and Venezuela

9. Descendants of Africans and European plantation colonists

10. Large plains, formed by erosion over millions of years, in Argentina

Multiple Choice

Circle the letter of the <u>best</u> answer.

11. Middle and South America's main energy resources are
    a. coal and nuclear power.
    b. solar energy and wind power.
    c. natural gas and geothermal energy.
    d. petroleum and hydroelectricity.

12. Many migrants moving from rural to urban areas in Middle and South America
    a. find work on nearby haciendas and plantations.
    b. are provided with free housing for six months.
    c. live in shantytowns surrounding the cities.
    d. join the military or work for the local government.

13. Many geographers believe that Mexico and Central America were formed when
    a. South America and Africa broke away from Gondwanaland.
    b. a jumble of small plates attached to the North American and Caribbean plates came together.
    c. South America rode up over the Nazca plate in the Pacific Ocean.
    d. the small Caribbean plate drifted eastward and collided with the large Pacific plate.

14. The three major river systems of South America are the
    a. Amazon, Paraná, and Orinoco.
    b. Río Negro, Rio Grande, and Río de la Plata.
    c. Paraguay, Uruguay, and São Francisco.
    d. Andes, Antilles, and Atacama.

15. The breaking up of large land holdings to allow more people to own their own land is called
    a. land reform.   b. commercial farming.
    c. sharecropping.   d. agribusiness.

16. The world's largest humid-tropical region is located
    a. in the forested area centered on the Amazon River.
    b. east of the Andes in southern Argentina.
    c. along the coast of southern Chile.
    d. in the forests of the Caribbean islands.

17. Which of the following is the best evidence of plate collision in Middle and South America?
    a. the large plains that cover much of the region
    b. the great river systems that flow throughout the region
    c. the Andes Mountains and earthquakes in Middle America
    d. the great extremes in climate across the region

18. The Monroe Doctrine
    a. announced the independence of former colonies in Middle and South America.
    b. established a fund for building dams, canals, and other major projects in Middle and South America.
    c. required Middle and South American countries to swear allegiance to the United States.
    d. declared Middle and South America off-limits to new European colonization.

19. The Aztecs and the Incas were
    a. names given to early Spanish and Portuguese settlers in South America.
    b. Native American civilizations conquered by Spanish explorers
    c. the first peoples in the Americas to defeat the Spanish explorers.
    d. the first Native American civilizations to build religious pyramids.

20. Some of the densest areas of settlement in Middle and South America are
    a. in the Amazon River Valley.
    b. at the southern tip of South America.
    c. along the border between Mexico and Guatemala.
    d. in the mountain valleys with mild climates.

Short Answer

Answer the questions in the space provided.

21. What is the Organization of American States (OAS)?

_____
_____
_____
_____
_____

22. List the names of the four major ancient monument-building Native American civilizations in Middle and South America. Where was each one based?

_____
_____
_____
_____
_____

Critical Thinking

Write your answers on a separate sheet of paper.

23. Describe the major challenges facing Middle and South America.

24. Compare and contrast the hacienda system with subsistence agriculture and agribusiness.

25. Why do you think European countries were so eager to colonize the Western Hemisphere?

CHAPTER 17

TEST ANSWERS

Matching

1. Answer: c Objective: 21

2. Answer: f Objective: 22

3. Answer: b Objective: 31

4. Answer: a Objective: 31

5. Answer: e Objective: 32

6. Answer: k Objective: 11

7. Answer: g Objective: 22

8. Answer: h Objective: 11

9. Answer: i Objective: 22

10. Answer: l Objective: 11

Multiple Choice

11. Answer: d Objective: 31

12. Answer: c Objective: 41

13. Answer: b Objective: 22

14. Answer: a Objective: 11

15. Answer: a Objective: 41

16. Answer: a Objective: 12

17. Answer: c Objective: 11

18. Answer: d Objective: 22

19. Answer: b Objective: 21

20. Answer: d Objective: 12

Short Answer

21. Answer:
    The OAS is made up of the United States and most of the countries of Middle and South America. The goals of the OAS are to keep peace in the Western Hemisphere, settle disputes among member nations, and foster cooperation in economic, social, and cultural affairs.

    Objective: 42

22. Answer:
The major ancient monument-building Native American civilizations in Middle and South America were the Olmecs in Mexico, the Mayas in Mexico and Central America, the Aztecs in central Mexico, and the Incas in western South America.

Objective: 21

Critical Thinking

23. Answer:
Possible answer: Middle and South America face many economic, social, and political challenges. Rapid population growth has placed a strain on already limited resources. Poverty and poor living conditions are widespread, especially in urban areas. Politically, many countries of the region are democratic but unstable. Different groups within wealthy families and the military have battled for political control, but changes in government have usually been minor, as wealth and land still remain in the hands of a few.
    Other challenges include foreign involvement in the region. Many people believe that foreign investment gives foreign countries too much control over Middle and South American affairs, and foreign loans, offered to stimulate development, have become a major problem for those countries that are unable to repay the debts. Also, some multinational companies have been accused of interfering in local politics and exploiting local resources.
    Another challenge to the region is halting the illegal drug trade. Some farmers decide to grow crops used for drugs because they can make more money than if they grew other kinds of crops.

Objective: 41

24. Answer:
Possible answer: Many haciendas are symbols of landowners' social status, rather than efficient farming operations. Because peasants have to split their time between farming their own crops and the landowners' crops, efficiency and maximum productivity are hard to achieve. In subsistence agriculture, farmers generally work their own fields exclusively, instead of dividing their labor as on a hacienda. Agribusiness is large-scale commercial agriculture, focused on exporting crops to international markets. It uses the latest farming methods and machinery, and, unlike subsistence agriculture and the hacienda system, does not require many farm workers.

Objective: 32

25. Answer:
Possible answer: They probably saw unlimited economic opportunities in the region as gold, silver, and land resources were plentiful. Countries with colonies often made large profits from developing these types of natural resources in their colonies. Colonizing countries also competed with each other, and the number, size, and location of a country's colonies contributed to its power and prestige.

Objective: 22

CHAPTER 18

TEST QUESTIONS

Matching

Match the term with its correct description. One term is not used.

a. Isthmus of Tehuantepec
b. privatization
c. monopoly
d. Sierra Madre Occidental
e. land reform
f. inflation

1. The mountain range that borders the Plateau of Mexico to the west

2. The rise in prices caused by a decrease in value of a nation's currency

3. The selling of government-owned businesses or lands to private owners

4. A narrow land area in southern Mexico that lies between the Gulf of Mexico and the Pacific Ocean

5. A business that has no competitors

Match the term with its correct description. One term is not used.

g. the Yucatán
h. cash crops
i. *maquiladoras*
j. Plateau of Mexico
k. *ejidos*
l. Greater Mexico City

6. Agricultural products grown primarily for direct sale in a market

7. Communal farms, once part of haciendas, divided into individual plots or farmed by groups of farmers

8. The Mexican culture region that holds more than one-fourth of Mexico's population

9. Factories established by U.S. and other foreign companies in Mexican border towns in which products for export are assembled

10. The region in southeastern Mexico that is famous for its resorts and Mayan ruins

Multiple Choice

Circle the letter of the <u>best</u> answer.

11. Mexico's economy began to improve quickly when
    a. many Mexicans started to migrate to Mexico City.
    b. inflation skyrocketed in the mid-1980s.
    c. Carlos Salinas de Gortari was elected president in 1988.
    d. the Institutional Revolutionary Party (PRI) was formed.

12. Mexico's major mineral resource is
    a. petroleum.   b. coal.
    c. copper.   d. iron ore.

13. The majority of Mexican workers are employed in
    a. agricultural and ranching jobs.
    b. government jobs.
    c. industrial and service jobs.
    d. mining jobs.

14. In Mexico's Central Interior region, one would most likely find
    a. *maquiladoras* in border towns.
    b. modern resort cities.
    c. oil refineries and petrochemical plants.
    d. old-style haciendas and colonial-style churches.

15. A major goal of the Mexican Revolution was to
    a. defeat the Institutional Revolutionary Party.
    b. declare the independence of the Valley of Mexico.
    c. increase the number of people who owned land.
    d. improve working conditions in the *maquiladoras.*

16. The variable that has the greatest influence on climate in most of Mexico is
    a. elevation.   b. vegetation.
    c. population.   d. pollution.

17. As a result of the removal of trade barriers and an increase in foreign competition, many
    of Mexico's industries
    a. are now run by managers from other countries.
    b. were purchased by the government.
    c. have become more efficient and productive.
    d. became monopolies.

18. The Mexican culture region in which indigenous languages are spoken by about half of the
    population is
    a. Northern Mexico.   b. the Oil Coast.
    c. Greater Mexico City.   d. Southern Mexico.

19. Mexico City sometimes experiences freezing temperatures as a result of
    a. tectonic activity in northern Mexico.
    b. precipitation at high elevations.
    c. polar air flowing southward across the Plateau of Mexico.
    d. cold ocean currents sweeping in from the Gulf of Mexico.

20. Mexican subsistence farmers grow traditional food crops such as
    a. maize (corn), beans, and squash.
    b. sugarcane and pineapples.
    c. coffee, cacao, and bananas.
    d. cotton, wheat, and alfalfa.

Short Answer

Answer the questions in the space provided.

21. How was the peninsula of Baja California formed? What results did its formation have for other parts of Mexico?

_____

_____

_____

_____

_____

22. Why have foreign companies established so many *maquiladoras* along the United States-Mexico border?

_____

_____

_____

_____

_____

Critical Thinking

Write your answers on a separate sheet of paper.

23. Compare and contrast two of the cultural regions of Mexico in terms of physical setting, population, economic activities, and resources. How do these traits explain each region's role in Mexico's economy?

24. In Mexico, privatization has been one factor contributing to an improvement in the country's economy. Explain how privatization can be an important step in economic recovery.

25. Would you like to live in Mexico City? Why or why not?

CHAPTER 18

TEST ANSWERS

Matching

1. Answer: d   Objective: 11

2. Answer: f   Objective: 41

3. Answer: b   Objective: 42

4. Answer: a   Objective: 11

5. Answer: c   Objective: 41

6. Answer: h   Objective: 21

7. Answer: k   Objective: 22

8. Answer: l   Objective: 32

9. Answer: i   Objective: 22

10. Answer: g   Objective: 32

Multiple Choice

11. Answer: c   Objective: 42

12. Answer: a   Objective: 21

13. Answer: c   Objective: 21

14. Answer: d   Objective: 32

15. Answer: c   Objective: 22

16. Answer: a   Objective: 12

17. Answer: c   Objective: 42

18. Answer: d   Objective: 32

19. Answer: c   Objective: 12

20. Answer: a   Objective: 21

Short Answer

21. Answer:
    Millions of years ago, Baja California was attached to the Mexican mainland. As the peninsula separated from the mainland and moved northwest, the Gulf of California opened, and an ocean trench developed off Mexico's Pacific coast. The heat and pressure along this trench have caused earthquakes and created volcanoes.

    Objective: 11

22. Answer:
   Foreign and U.S. companies have established factories along the border to take advantage of Mexico's lower wages. Cities in northern Mexico have close economic ties with many southern U.S. cities.

   Objective: 22

Critical Thinking

23. Answer:
   Students may compare and/or contrast any two of the six regions, including Greater Mexico City, the Central Interior, the oil coast, southern Mexico, northern Mexico, and the Yucatán. Students should give information about both regions' physical, human, and economic characteristics. Likely responses may compare and contrast northern Mexico and southern Mexico, the oil coast and the Yucatán, and Greater Mexico City and the Central Interior.

   Objective: 31

24. Answer:
   Possible answer: Privatization can assist the government by providing it with cash to pay off debts and invest in new projects, and by relieving it of management responsibility and costs. Individuals who buy government-owned businesses or lands may have more capital than the government to create a greater profit. They may also have increased motivation to succeed financially because their future existence is no longer guaranteed and because they have a greater personal stake in the enterprise.

   Objective: 42

25. Answer:
   Answers will vary. Students interested in living in Mexico City might be attracted to the city's museums, universities, and other cultural features. Most should recognize that life in the city is better for those who are wealthy. Students not interested in living in Mexico City might mention pollution, poverty, unemployment, slums, and congestion.

   Objective: 32

CHAPTER 19

TEST QUESTIONS

Matching

Match the term with its correct description. One term is not used.

a. commonwealth
b. merengue
c. Nicaragua
d. cardamom
e. Panama
f. cooperative

1. An organization owned by and operated for the mutual benefit of its members

2. A spice grown in the central highlands of Guatemala

3. The national music and dance of the Dominican Republic

4. A self-governing political unit

5. A newly democratic country with a broad, tectonically active, inland valley containing large lakes

Match the term with its correct description. One term is not used.

g. voodoo
h. plantain
i. calypso
j. manioc
k. refugee
l. reggae

6. A type of banana used in cooking

7. A person who flees his or her own country, often for economic or political reasons

8. A form of music that originated in Trinidad and Tobago

9. A religion, commonly practiced in Haiti, whose followers believe that spirits of good and evil play an important part in daily life

10. A form of music that originated in Jamaica

Multiple Choice

Circle the letter of the <u>best</u> answer.

11. Panama's coastal plains
    a. are located only in the western part of the country.
    b. have a high elevation.
    c. are located only next to the Panama Canal.
    d. are narrow due to the country's mostly mountainous terrain.

12. The settlement of Belize was limited for many years by the country's
    a. humid-tropical climate and thick forests.
    b. cold, high plains.
    c. small indigenous population.
    d. rebellious plantation owners in the highlands.

13. The climate of the Caribbean islands is
    a. humid tropical.   b. Mediterranean.
    c. steppe.   d. humid continental.

14. A major export crop of many Central American countries is
    a. soybeans.   b. maize (corn).
    c. wheat.   d. coffee.

15. Nearly all Caribbean islands today
    a. still show the effects of colonialism and slavery.
    b. profit from subsistence farming.
    c. have low unemployment and high wages.
    d. have rich deposits of oil and bauxite.

16. The Central American country with the highest standard of living and literacy rate is
    a. Honduras.   b. Costa Rica.
    c. Belize.   d. Nicaragua.

17. A rapidly growing industry in the Caribbean islands is
    a. silver mining.   b. automobile manufacturing.
    c. tourism.   d. oil refining.

18. A continuing issue for Guatemala, El Salvador, and Nicaragua is
    a. coastal development.   b. land reform.
    c. fishing rights.   d. political independence.

19. Cuba must import much of its food because it
    a. is mostly mountainous and dry, with poor soils.
    b. still relies on trade with and aid from the Soviet Union.
    c. uses most of its farmland to grow sugarcane, a cash crop.
    d. relies on the manufacture of consumer goods for most of its income.

20. The inland regions of Central America have a milder climate than the coastal regions because of
    a. mountain elevations.   b. warm trade winds.
    c. more abundant rainfall.   d. Pacific Ocean currents.

Short Answer

Answer the questions in the space provided.

21. Why does modern Panama seem like three separate countries to some people?
    _____
    _____
    _____
    _____
    _____

22. Why do some of the Caribbean islands regularly experience drought conditions despite frequent rains?
    _____
    _____
    _____
    _____
    _____

128

Critical Thinking

Write your answers on a separate sheet of paper.

23. Explain how regional cooperation could help solve some of the problems facing Central America.

24. In the year 2000, control of the Panama Canal will shift from the United States to Panama. How do you think this event will affect these two countries?

25. There is debate about how much the United States should help Haitian refugees and refugees from other troubled areas who appeal for assistance and protection. Do you think the United States should help the Haitian refugees? Why or why not?

CHAPTER 19

TEST ANSWERS

Matching

1. Answer: f Objective: 22

2. Answer: d Objective: 12

3. Answer: b Objective: 22

4. Answer: a Objective: 22

5. Answer: c Objective: 11

6. Answer: h Objective: 22

7. Answer: k Objective: 22

8. Answer: i Objective: 22

9. Answer: g Objective: 22

10. Answer: l Objective: 22

Multiple Choice

11. Answer: d Objective: 11

12. Answer: a Objective: 11

13. Answer: a Objective: 21

14. Answer: d Objective: 12

15. Answer: a Objective: 22

16. Answer: b Objective: 12

17. Answer: c Objective: 22

18. Answer: b Objective: 12

19. Answer: c Objective: 22

20. Answer: a Objective: 11

Short Answer

21. Answer:
    Panama has three very physically and culturally different regions—the nearly uninhabited forested area in the east, the prosperous urban area surrounding the Panama Canal, and the more rural farming areas in the western part of the country.
    Objective: 12

22. Answer:
Although it rains often on the islands, several, such as Jamaica and Puerto Rico, have many limestone rocks through which water rapidly drains. Thus soil cannot hold the moisture from the rains.

Objective: 21

Critical Thinking

23. Answer:
Possible answer: Central American countries might be able to gain strength and solve their problems through unity. Since the countries of Central America have similar environments, they grow similar export crops. Instead of competing with each other, they might form an economic association in which they sell their export crops as one group and then share the profits. They might even have each country produce only one of several cash crops for export and devote the rest of their land to food production. All of the countries could benefit from the profits of the group as a whole and decrease their food imports.

Furthermore, the political instability within the region has discouraged foreign investment, which would aid development. The region might show a united front by developing a regional policy regarding the behavior of governments in the region. They might form an organization that would monitor the region and its governments and protect citizens' rights. This effort would show the world that the region is committed to stability and growth.

Objective: 12

24. Answer:
Possible answer: Panama will probably benefit economically, and may become a more powerful force in the region. The United States may have to pay more money to ship goods through the canal, and it will lose some of its control over political and economic affairs in the region.

Objective: 12

25. Answer:
Answers will vary. Students arguing that the United States should help the Haitians will probably point to the poverty and political problems in Haiti. They might say that the Haitians would not ask for help unless conditions were intolerable, and that America has a moral obligation to help them. Others might argue that the United States has enough problems of its own to solve, and that the United States cannot and should not solve the problems of other countries.

Objective: 22

CHAPTER 20

TEST QUESTIONS

Matching

Match the term with its correct description. One term is not used.

a. *páramo*
b. Venezuela
c. *tierra fría*
d. Suriname
e. guerrilla
f. Colombia

1. The Andes elevation zone that extends from about 6,000 feet (1,829 m) to 10,000 feet (3,048 m) and has cool forests and grasslands

2. The Andes elevation zone that extends from about 10,000 feet (3,048m) to 16,000 feet (4,877 m), where llamas, alpacas, and sheep graze and nighttime frosts are common

3. A person who participates in irregular warfare as a member of an armed band

4. The only South American country with coastlines on both the Caribbean Sea and the Pacific Ocean

5. A country that receives most of its income from its oil and mineral wealth

Match the term with its correct description. One term is not used.

g. *tierra templada*
h. bauxite
i. cacao
j. *tierra caliente*
k. *tierra helada*
l. llanos

6. The Andes zone of highest elevation, permanently covered with snow

7. The hot and humid lowest Andes elevation zone, between sea level and 3,000 feet (914 m)

8. A region in Venezuela of short-tree and grass savannas, where cattle graze

9. An important mineral resource of Guyana and Suriname

10. The Andes elevation zone with a cool, moist climate that supports the growth of many types of crops

Multiple Choice

Circle the letter of the <u>best</u> answer.

11. One landform region shared by both Venezuela and Colombia is the
    a. Guiana Highlands.   b. Amazon Basin.
    c. Andes Mountains.   d. Pacific Lowlands.

12. Cutting and setting fire to forests to clear land for planting is called
    a. the hacienda system.
    b. tropical forest farming.
    c. plantation agriculture.
    d. slash-and-burn farming.

13. If you work on a cacao or banana plantation in the Andes region, you probably live in the
    a. *tierra fría.*
    b. *tierra caliente.*
    c. *tierra helada.*
    d. *tierra templada.*

14. The population of Guyana is made up mostly of
    a. people of South Asian and African descent.
    b. emigrants from France and the United States.
    c. former Dutch colonists and Roman Catholics.
    d. indigenous South Americans.

15. At least 90 percent of the world's emeralds and much of its coffee come from
    a. Venezuela.
    b. Guyana.
    c. Colombia.
    d. French Guiana.

16. Much of the recent violence in Colombia has been related to
    a. conflicts between landowners and farmers.
    b. the illegal drug trade.
    c. competition for oil profits.
    d. the struggle for independence from France.

17. An item you might buy that would be least likely to be made from a product from this region is a
    a. bouquet of flowers.
    b. box of aluminum foil.
    c. pair of pearl earrings.
    d. bag of sugar.

18. Venezuela might be described as a nation of contrasts, with
    a. steep cliffs in the northern highlands and enormous, flat plains, or llanos, to the south.
    b. colonial and communist institutions existing side by side.
    c. humid climates in the coastal regions and arid climates in the highland regions.
    d. most of the country's wealthy people living in rural areas and almost all of its poor people living in the cities.

19. Venezuela's capital city, which has a new modern subway, is
    a. Bogotá.   b. Cartagena.   c. Paramaribo.   d. Caracas.

20. Guyana and Suriname experience political tension because of the
    a. military forces in power.
    b. differences among various ethnic groups.
    c. revolutionary activity against colonial rule.
    d. dispute with Venezuela over territory.

Short Answer

Answer the questions in the space provided.

21. How have the Andes hindered communication and transportation in Colombia? How have these problems been improved?
    _____
    _____
    _____
    _____
    _____

22. What problem is associated with oil profits in Venezuela? How is the government trying to overcome this problem?

_____
_____
_____
_____
_____
_____

Critical Thinking

Write your answers on a separate sheet of paper.

23. Compare and contrast the resources and governments of Venezuela and Colombia to determine why Venezuela has become the economic and political leader of the region.

24. Guyana and Suriname were once colonies, and French Guiana is still a territory of France. What about these countries' location might have made them attractive to colonizing European powers?

25. Do you think it would be possible to stop the flow of illegal drugs from Colombia without seriously harming that nation's economy? Explain.

CHAPTER 20

TEST ANSWERS

Matching

1. Answer: c Objective: 11

2. Answer: a Objective: 11

3. Answer: e Objective: 12

4. Answer: f Objective: 11

5. Answer: b Objective: 22

6. Answer: k Objective: 11

7. Answer: j Objective: 11

8. Answer: l Objective: 21

9. Answer: h Objective: 31

10. Answer: g Objective: 11

Multiple Choice

11. Answer: c Objective: 11

12. Answer: d Objective: 22

13. Answer: b Objective: 11

14. Answer: a Objective: 32

15. Answer: c Objective: 12

16. Answer: b Objective: 12

17. Answer: c Objective: 31

18. Answer: a Objective: 21

19. Answer: d Objective: 22

20. Answer: b Objective: 32

Short Answer

21. Answer:
The Andes lie between the Caribbean and Pacific regions of the country, thereby blocking easy travel between the two coasts. Communication and transportation have improved, however, with the opening of the Panama Canal, road construction, and the development of air transportation.

Objective: 11

22. Answer:

The country's economy has become dependent on oil revenues. When oil prices drop, the country suffers. The government is trying to reduce the economy's dependence on oil by encouraging the growth of new industries.

Objective: 22

Critical Thinking

23. Answer:

Possible answer: Both Venezuela and Colombia have plentiful natural resources, and the Andes provide the countries with different climates that support a great variety of crops. Both have rich mineral resources. Venezuela has vast oil deposits as well as large deposits of iron ore and other minerals. Hydroelectric power and oil have helped develop the country's steel industry. Though not as oil-rich as Venezuela, Colombia also has oil deposits, as well as 90 percent of the world's emeralds. It also produces iron ore, and coffee and flowers are important agricultural exports. Colombia has a good trade location and improved interior transportation. The nation, however, is politically unstable. It is troubled by violence and corruption, much of which stems from the illegal drug trade. These problems make it difficult for Colombia to provide economic and political leadership for its own people, let alone the region. Venezuela, on the other hand, has a more stable government that has been able to use the country's oil profits to help its people and to become a powerful force in the region.

Objective: 22

24. Answer:

Possible answer: All three countries are located on the continent's northern coast. They are easily accessible from the Caribbean Sea and the Atlantic Ocean. They are thus important for trade.

Objective: 32

25. Answer:

Answers will vary. Students might suggest that the Colombian government will need to provide other economic incentives for people now involved in the illegal drug trade—jobs, land, and so on. To do this, the country might require assistance from other countries. Some students might point out that economic aid from foreign countries to Colombia might not only help Colombia but might also help the aiding countries themselves if the drug trade is reduced, since the drug trade is an international problem.

Objective: 12

CHAPTER 21

TEST QUESTIONS

Matching

Match the term with its correct description. One term is not used.

a. growth pole
b. Campo Cerrado
c. soil exhaustion
d. Belo Horizonte
e. landlocked country
f. buffer state

1. A frontier region in Brazil, in which the city of Brasília is located

2. A small country that separates two larger competing countries

3. A metropolitan area given official help to strengthen its economic development

4. A city in Brazil's Southeast region, near which much of Brazil's mining and many industries are located

5. The loss in nutrients that results from always planting the same crop in a particular area

Match the term with its correct description. One term is not used.

g. pampas
h. *favelas*
i. Guaraní
j. Chaco
k. yerba mate
l. tannin

6. Huge slum areas found around many of Brazil's cities

7. An indigenous language spoken by about 95 percent of Paraguay's people

8. The wide grassy plains that make up Argentina's most densely settled region

9. A substance used in preparing leather

10. A region of low plains and dry forests and savannas in northern Argentina

Multiple Choice

Circle the letter of the best answer.

11. Both Argentina and Uruguay have
    a. a low literacy rate and a small middle class.
    b. desert climates and high mountains.
    c. strong democratic traditions.
    d. humid-subtropical climates and rich soils.

12. Since the 1970s and 1980s, Brazil's economy has weakened as a result of
    a. problems in the coffee-producing industry.
    b. the accumulation of an enormous foreign debt.
    c. labor unrest in urban areas along the coast.
    d. the development of the Campo Cerrado and Amazon regions.

13. Most of Brazil is made up of
    a. lowland plains and level plateaus.
    b. swampy deltas and marshes.
    c. eroded mountains and river valleys.
    d. deserts and arid savannas.

14. Population in Argentina's Patagonia region will probably increase when
    a. the region becomes independent from the United Kingdom.
    b. the region's forests are cleared to allow settlement.
    c. oil deposits off the coast of the region are further developed.
    d. modern agricultural methods are adopted in the region.

15. Argentina's main source of wealth comes from
    a. oil.   b. logging.
    c. mining.   d. agriculture.

16. Early settlers to Brazil affected the country's physical geography by
    a. replacing tropical forests along the Atlantic coast with sugar plantations.
    b. widening the Río de la Plata so that ships could reach the interior of the country.
    c. building roads and developing mining projects in the Amazon region.
    d. dividing the pampas into ranches and fencing in livestock.

17. Brazil's most prosperous region, where most of the country's people live, is the
    a. Campo Cerrado.   b. Northeast.
    c. Southeast.   d. Amazon.

18. A landlocked nation is one that
    a. has large areas of farmland surrounding crowded urban areas.
    b. is completely surrounded by other countries and blocked from direct access to the ocean.
    c. prevents its people from traveling to surrounding countries.
    d. has fortified borders.

19. A major obstacle to economic progress in Argentina has been
    a. the country's need to import food.
    b. extended periods of drought.
    c. a decline in population.
    d. political instability.

20. Both Uruguay and Paraguay are major producers of
    a. tannin.   b. hydroelectricity.
    c. wool.   d. quebracho.

Short Answer

Answer the questions in the space provided.

21. Describe Brazil's three landform and climate regions.

    _____
    _____
    _____
    _____
    _____
    _____

22. How did the 1982 conflict over the Falkland Islands affect Argentina's government?

_____
_____
_____
_____
_____
_____

Critical Thinking

Write your answers on a separate sheet of paper.

23. Describe the locations of the capital cities of Brazil, Argentina, and Uruguay. What geographical characteristics, natural resources, and economic activity may account for the development of these cities as major economic centers?

24. Agree or disagree with the following statement: "Brazil's Amazon region is best left undeveloped." Explain your answer.

25. If you were the president of Uruguay, to lessen rural poverty would you encourage people from rural areas to move to the cities? Or would you focus on land reform? Explain.

CHAPTER 21

TEST ANSWERS

Matching

1. Answer: b Objective: 12

2. Answer: f Objective: 31

3. Answer: a Objective: 12

4. Answer: d Objective: 12

5. Answer: c Objective: 11

6. Answer: h Objective: 12

7. Answer: i Objective: 32

8. Answer: g Objective: 21

9. Answer: l Objective: 22

10. Answer: j Objective: 21

Multiple Choice

11. Answer: d Objective: 21

12. Answer: b Objective: 12

13. Answer: a Objective: 11

14. Answer: c Objective: 21

15. Answer: d Objective: 22

16. Answer: a Objective: 11

17. Answer: c Objective: 12

18. Answer: b Objective: 32

19. Answer: d Objective: 22

20. Answer: b Objective: 31

Short Answer

21. Answer:
    Brazil's three landform and climate regions are the Amazon region in the north, which has rolling plains, huge rain forests, and a humid-tropical climate; the Brazilian Highlands along the east coast, which are old eroded mountains that have a variety of climates ranging from semiarid to marine west coast; and the Brazilian Plateau, a humid region of upland plains covered by savanna woodlands.

    Objective: 11

22. Answer:
Argentina's military government invaded the Falklands, a United Kingdom territory, in 1982. When Argentina was defeated in a brief war with the United Kingdom, political power in Argentina was returned to a civilian democratic government.

Objective: 22

Critical Thinking

23. Answer:
Possible answer: The capital cities of the eastern South American countries are generally located in regions with conditions favorable for farming, business, trade, and/or industry. Brasília, Brazil's modern capital city, was built about 600 miles (965 km) from the coast. Its location was deliberately chosen to encourage development in the country's interior region. Much of the Campo Cerrado, where Brasília is located, is being developed as an agricultural region.

The capital of Argentina, Buenos Aires, is located in the heart of Argentina's most productive region—the pampas. More than one third of Argentina's people and a large number of its industries are located in or near this capital city. Furthermore, Buenos Aires' situation on the Río de la Plata, the major waterway of southern South America, provides an excellent location for export trade.

As with Buenos Aires, the location of Montevideo on the Río de la Plata estuary is probably a major reason for its development as Uruguay's business and government center. Montevideo is also Uruguay's most prosperous area.

Objective: 12

24. Answer:
Answers will vary but should reflect a weighing of the advantages and disadvantages of developing the Amazon region. Developing the Amazon might provide additional land for settlement and jobs processing the region's products. The further destruction of the forests, however, may cause irreparable damage to plants, animals, and worldwide climate patterns. Conflicts with Native Americans who will lose their forest homes may increase. Furthermore, industrial development may pollute the Amazon River. Students should provide clear reasons for their positions.

Objective: 12

25. Answer:
Answers will vary. Students supporting urban growth might point to the lack of opportunity in rural areas. They might argue that Uruguay could become more of an industrial power with a larger urban population. On the other hand, problems with urban growth include overcrowding, poverty, unemployment, pollution, and poor health and living conditions. Students supporting land reform might consider the example of other countries, such as Mexico, which have experienced some success. Land reform might make agriculture, currently practiced on haciendas, more productive, thus creating more prosperity in the rural areas of the country. Land reform, however, often is a slow process and may be politically unpopular with the owners of large estates.

Objective: 31

CHAPTER 22

TEST QUESTIONS

Matching

Match the term with its correct description. One term is not used.

a. *altiplano*
b. *minifundio*
c. El Niño
d. *selvas*
e. Oriente
f. *latifundia*

1. A broad highland plain between the eastern and western ridges of the Andes in Peru and Bolivia

2. A South American land tenure system in which tenant farmers work on large estates in exchange for food

3. The local name for the thick rain-forest vegetation in Ecuador's eastern region

4. An unusual global weather pattern, occurring every five to ten years, that involves a warming of the coastal waters of Peru and Ecuador and can cause severe flooding

5. One of several family farms created from the division of a large estate into many parts

Match the term with its correct description. One term is not used.

g. inflation
h. cartel
i. Sierra
j. terrorism
k. Quechua
l. coup

6. An overthrow of an existing government by another political or military group

7. Ecuador's mountain region, in which almost half of the country's people live

8. A group of business organizations that agree to limit supplies of a product and thereby keep prices high

9. The use of violence as a means of political force

10. An ancient language spoken by many Native Americans in Ecuador and Peru

Multiple Choice

Circle the letter of the <u>best</u> answer.

11. One of the densest areas of Native American settlement in the Americas is the
    a. *altiplano* region of Peru's Andes highlands.
    b. Costa region of Ecuador.
    c. eastern highlands of Bolivia.
    d. broad central valley of Chile.

12. Ecuador's most important agricultural region, where many export crops are grown, is the
    a. *selvas.*   b. Costa.
    c. Sierra.   d. Oriente.

13. Because of the tourist trade on the Galápagos Islands,
    a. more than 10,000 people live on the islands.
    b. the islands are becoming an important financial center.
    c. native speakers of Quechua have had to learn Spanish.
    d. the islands' natural environments are being threatened.

14. Much of northern Chile's income comes from
    a. subsistence farming.   b. mining.
    c. high-tech industries.   d. service industries.

15. In Chile, the trend in agriculture is to
    a. combine small pieces of land to form large estates.
    b. produce fruits for export on commercial farms.
    c. irrigate areas in the far south.
    d. limit production to wheat and dairy products.

16. Bolivia's eastern lowlands remain mostly undeveloped because the region
    a. is in the northern part of the Atacama Desert.
    b. has poor soils and inadequate rainfall.
    c. lacks roads, people, and money for investment.
    d. has been the target of a conflict between wealthy families.

17. Lake Titicaca is unique because it is the
    a. highest lake in the world on which ships travel.
    b. source of all of Chile's drinking water.
    c. only place in South America where Incans still live.
    d. largest saltwater lake in the Western Hemisphere.

18. A major concern in Peru's Oriente region is how to
    a. manage and preserve the Incan ruins of Machu Picchu.
    b. preserve the rain forests being cleared by subsistence farmers.
    c. protect villages from the heavy flooding caused by El Niño.
    d. irrigate the dry coastal plains of the Amazon Basin.

19. Ecuador's *selvas* is located
    a. between the two high mountain ranges in central Ecuador.
    b. west of the Costa region along the Atlantic coast.
    c. in the eastern savannas along the Pacific coast.
    d. in the humid-tropical lowlands of the Oriente.

20. Peru has experienced inflation because
    a. terrorism has caused prices to fall as a result of the scarcity of goods.
    b. the government has had to print more money to manage a growing foreign debt.
    c. its military government uses free-market practices.
    d. more and more people are moving from the highlands to Lima and Callao.

Short Answer

Answer the questions in the space provided.

21. Why is Ecuador's Costa a richer agricultural region than Peru's coastal areas?

_____
_____
_____
_____
_____

22. Explain the historical significance of Quito.

_____
_____
_____
_____
_____

Critical Thinking

Write your answers on a separate sheet of paper.

23. What regions of Ecuador, Peru, Bolivia, and Chile show the greatest economic promise? Describe the characteristics that will attract people to these regions in the future.

24. Why do you think El Niño affects weather patterns around the world?

25. Do you think Chile should establish a cartel to control copper prices? If Chile invited other copper-producing nations to be part of the cartel, do you think it would be to the advantage of these nations to join? Why or why not?

CHAPTER 22

TEST ANSWERS

Matching

    1.Answer: a Objective: 21

    2.Answer: f Objective: 32

    3.Answer: d Objective: 11

    4.Answer: c Objective: 22

    5.Answer: b Objective: 32

    6.Answer: l Objective: 32

    7.Answer: i Objective: 12

    8.Answer: h Objective: 32

    9.Answer: j Objective: 22

    10.Answer: k Objective: 12

Multiple Choice

    11.Answer: a Objective: 21

    12.Answer: b Objective: 11

    13.Answer: d Objective: 11

    14.Answer: b Objective: 31

    15.Answer: b Objective: 32

    16.Answer: c Objective: 31

    17.Answer: a Objective: 31

    18.Answer: b Objective: 22

    19.Answer: d Objective: 11

    20.Answer: b Objective: 22

Short Answer

21.Answer:
Most of Ecuador's Pacific coast is made up of fertile lowlands, most of which have a humid-tropical or savanna climate. Peru's coastal areas, on the other hand, are mostly rugged and dry. A cool ocean current and the rain shadow-effect caused by the Andes keep the region a desert.

Objective: 21

22. Answer:

Quito was once a northern kingdom of the Incan Empire. Later, it became the center for Spanish colonial government. It still has many old churches and monuments that are reminiscent of the colonial era.

Objective: 12

Critical Thinking

23. Answer:

Possible answer: In Ecuador, the Costa continues to grow; in both Ecuador and Peru, the Oriente has great economic promise; in Bolivia, the most promising region is the eastern lowlands; and in Chile, it is the far southern part of the country. Ecuador's Costa has rich agricultural potential, rich fishing grounds, and natural-gas deposits. The Oriente of Ecuador and Peru provides lumber and tree crops such as rubber, and is being cleared for more farmland by subsistence farmers. The greatest resource of the Oriente, however, is oil, particularly in Ecuador. Preserving the rain forests is the greatest environmental concern raised by development in this region. In Bolivia, the eastern lowlands have the potential to be a prosperous region for farming, with fertile soils and good rainfall, and grazing cattle. In addition, recent oil discoveries may make this region more important in the future. In far southern Chile, large forests could provide lumber, and there are large deposits of coal and oil in this region as well.

Objective: 12

24. Answer:

Possible answer: El Niño conditions are probably caused by the build-up of unusually warm waters in the mid-Pacific Ocean. Since ocean currents are one of the major ways by which heat is moved among the different parts of the world, and thus have a significant influence on global climates, changes to ocean waters and currents have the ability to affect world weather patterns.

Objective: 22

25. Answer:

Answers will vary. Some students might say that since copper is such an important part of Chile's export economy, Chile is vulnerable when copper prices fluctuate on the world market. Forming a cartel to keep copper prices high might protect and even improve Chile's economy. If the cartel established by Chile included other copper-producing nations, these nations might experience the same benefits. However, they might also have less control over their own economic policies.

Objective: 32

UNIT 4

TEST QUESTIONS

Matching

Match the term with its correct description. One term is not used.

a. *altiplano*
b. plantain
c. hacienda
d. inflation
e. *maquiladora*
f. cartel

1. An agreement among producers to regulate the supply of a product, thereby giving them increased control over prices

2. A broad highland plain between the eastern and western ridges of the Andes

3. A large family-owned estate in Middle and South America on which farmers work for a landowner in payment for small plots of land and services provided by the landowner

4. The rise in prices caused by a decrease in the value of a nation's currency

5. A factory, established by a foreign country near the Mexican border, in which export products are assembled

Match the term with its correct description. One term is not used.

g. Mayas
h. llanos
i. *selvas*
j. Incas
k. mestizos
l. guerillas

6. Native Americans who flourished in present-day Mexico and Central America between about A.D. 250 and 900

7. People with both Native American and European ancestors

8. Thick rain forest vegetation in South America

9. Large plains in northern South America, formed by erosion over millions of years

10. A once-powerful Native American civilization of the Andes region

Multiple Choice

Circle the letter of the best answer.

11. The sharp contrast in development among the regions within each of the Andean countries exists partly because of
    a. a lack of good transportation.
    b. dramatic industrial growth in the countries of Caribbean and Atlantic South America.
    c. the scarcity of energy resources throughout all of the regions.
    d. the success of land reform in mountain areas.

12. Both Mexico and Venezuela have experienced rapid economic progress over the past few decades largely because of
    a. a booming tourist trade.
    b. profits gained from oil deposits.
    c. expansion of food-processing industries.
    d. development of copper resources.

13. The Andes elevation zone in which most of Ecuador's Costa region is located is the
    a. *páramo.*
    b. *tierra caliente.*
    c. *tierra helada.*
    d. *tierra fría.*

14. The theory of plate tectonics helps to explain the
    a. formation of the Andes Mountains, Mexico, and Central America.
    b. relationship between altitude and climate in South America.
    c. settlement patterns in the valleys of the Andes Mountains.
    d. occurrence of the El Niño weather pattern every five to ten years.

15. Far southern Chile and Argentina's Patagonia region are sparsely populated because these regions
    a. lack valuable resources for development.
    b. are covered with dense tropical forests.
    c. have climates that are too harsh for widespread settlement.
    d. are covered with glaciers.

16. Changes to Middle and South America brought by European colonists included all of the following except
    a. the establishment of plantations in the Caribbean Islands.
    b. the introduction of European crops, livestock, and farming methods.
    c. the expansion of the Native Americans' gold and silver mines.
    d. the establishment of Communist governments in Mexico and Peru.

17. Hydroelectric projects are as important to Paraguay's future growth as
    a. coffee production is to Mexico's.
    b. tin exports are to Bolivia's.
    c. oil resources are to Colombia's.
    d. sugarcane plantations are to El Salvador's.

18. All of the following statements are false except
    a. South America contains the largest humid-tropical climate region in the world.
    b. The driest region of Middle and South America is Mexico's Yucatán Peninsula.
    c. Southern South America is dominated by a subarctic climate.
    d. El Niño causes heavy rainfall in Paraguay, Jamaica, and Argentina.

19. Ethnic conflicts have created much tension in
    a. Venezuela and Uruguay.
    b. Haiti and Nicaragua.
    c. Costa Rica and Argentina.
    d. Suriname and Guyana.

20. All of the following are major challenges facing the Middle and South American region except

    a. rapid population growth.

    b. political instability.

    c. land reform.

    d. the decline of manufacturing industries.

Short Answer

Answer the questions in the space provided.

21. Why has the Amazon region remained largely undeveloped until recently?

_____

_____

_____

_____

_____

22. What caused the decline of the great Native American civilizations of Middle and South America?

_____

_____

_____

_____

_____

Critical Thinking

Write your answers on a separate sheet of paper.

23. Imagine the year is 2025. Select any Middle or South American country discussed in the unit, and write a paragraph explaining how the country has changed since the 1990s. Base your information on your own creativity and logical reasoning as well as on material in the textbook.

24. What effect do the Andes Mountains have on where South Americans live?

25. Shantytowns, such as Brazil's *favelas,* are found not just in Middle and South America but in many countries around the world. How do shantytowns form? How might life in shantytowns be improved?

UNIT 4

TEST ANSWERS

Matching

1. Answer: f Objective: 45

2. Answer: a Objective: 41

3. Answer: c Objective: 44

4. Answer: d Objective: 45

5. Answer: e Objective: 45

6. Answer: g Objective: 43

7. Answer: k Objective: 44

8. Answer: i Objective: 41

9. Answer: h Objective: 41

10. Answer: j Objective: 43

Multiple Choice

11. Answer: a Objective: 45

12. Answer: b Objective: 42

13. Answer: b Objective: 41

14. Answer: a Objective: 41

15. Answer: c Objective: 41

16. Answer: d Objective: 44

17. Answer: c Objective: 42

18. Answer: a Objective: 41

19. Answer: d Objective: 45

20. Answer: d Objective: 45

Short Answer

21. Answer:
    The region's humid-tropical climate and dense forests, as well as its remoteness from urban areas, have made transportation difficult and have limited settlement.

    Objective: 42

22. Answer:
A variety of factors led to the downfall of these civilizations, such as those of the Aztecs and Incas. When Europeans arrived, they had guns and armor that gave them an advantage in warfare. The Europeans also brought to the region certain diseases to which the Native Americans had no resistance.

Objective: 44

Critical Thinking

23. Answer:
Answers will vary. Paragraphs should be creative, well-reasoned, and realistic discussions of economic, political, and/or social changes that any Middle or South American country might experience between the 1990s and 2025. Possible topics include changes in Panama due to its new control of the Panama Canal, the political status of Puerto Rico, whether Venezuela remains dependent on oil, the status of the Brazilian rain forests, and how Peru has managed its foreign debt.

Objective: 45

24. Answer:
Possible answer: The Andes Mountains help to create the dry climates of southern Argentina and the deserts along the Pacific coast, discouraging dense settlement in these regions. Western Peru is populated mainly in the river valleys that get their water from melted Andean snow. The population supported at different altitude zones of the Andes reflects the highland climates and the quality and quantity of crops that can be grown.

Objective: 41

25. Answer:
Shantytowns form when people from rural areas move to cities, have difficulty finding work, and cannot afford to live but in the most basic of shelters around cities' edges. Answers to the second part will vary. Students might say that city governments should take responsibility for providing services such as running water, waste disposal, and health care to residents of shantytowns. City and national governments might also work to improve rural life so fewer rural dwellers would migrate to the cities.

Objective: 45

CHAPTER 23

TEST QUESTIONS

Matching

Match the term with its correct description. One term is not used.

a. famine
b. natural boundary
c. reunification
d. balance of power
e. microstate
f. icebreaker

1. A condition that exists when members of a group have equal levels of strength

2. A very small country

3. A ship that keeps frozen sea lanes open for other ships

4. The process of rejoining parts into one unit

5. A physical feature that establishes a political border between countries

Match the term with its correct description. One term is not used.

g. European Community (EC)
h. imperialism
i. navigable
j. economic association
k. Eurasia
l. multilingual

6. Able to be sailed by large ships, such as a wide and deep river

7. The world's largest landmass, made up of the continents of Europe and Asia

8. An association, formed in 1957, of several European nations that together are the world's largest exporter

9. The policy of gaining control over territory outside one's own nation

10. Having the ability to speak three or more languages

Multiple Choice

Circle the letter of the best answer.

11. The religion practiced by most people in Southern Europe is
    a. Roman Catholicism.
    c. Islam.
    b. Judaism.
    d. Protestantism.

12. Europe's ancient eroded landform region consisting of rugged hills and low mountains is the
   a. Northwest Highlands.
   b. Alpine mountain system.
   c. Northern European Plain.
   d. Central Uplands.

13. The climate found in most of Northern and West Central Europe is
   a. humid subtropical.
   b. Mediterranean.
   c. tundra.
   d. marine west coast.

14. All of the following are challenges faced by Europe today except
   a. environmental pollution.
   b. high birthrates.
   c. ethnic tensions.
   d. terrorism.

15. Much of Eastern Europe trails western Europe in agricultural production because
   a. its soils are poorer than those of western Europe.
   b. its farming technology is less advanced than that of western Europe.
   c. it is covered by dense forests.
   d. its people have devoted their efforts to developing the region's rich oil resources.

16. The major factor that creates mild climate conditions throughout much of Europe is the
   a. moderating effect of the Atlantic Ocean on the region.
   b. far northern location of the region.
   c. number of peninsulas and mountains in the region.
   d. region's close proximity to the equator.

17. What the Black Forest, the Ardennes, and the Massif Central have in common is that they are all
   a. unpopulated regions.
   b. forests located in Germany.
   c. part of the Central Uplands region.
   d. natural boundaries of the Northwest Highlands region.

18. Most of Europe's energy needs are met by
   a. coal mines in Great Britain.
   b. imports of oil and gas from other regions.
   c. solar energy.
   d. hydroelectric power.

19. The first European nations to establish large foreign colonies during the sixteenth and seventeenth centuries were
   a. Spain and Portugal.
   b. France and Belgium.
   c. Great Britain and Germany.
   d. Denmark and Italy.

20. The purpose of economic associations, such as the EC, is to
   a. create new tariffs on goods traded among its members.
   b. promote democracy in Communist countries.
   c. break down trade barriers among member nations.
   d. import raw materials from colonies.

Short Answer

Answer the questions in the space provided.

21. Explain why Europe is ideally suited for trade by sea.
   _____
   _____
   _____
   _____
   _____

22. What is an alliance? Describe the two major alliances formed in Europe in the decade following World War II.

_____
_____
_____
_____
_____
_____

Critical Thinking

Write your answers on a separate sheet of paper.

23. What role has water played in the political and economic development of Europe?

24. Many European nations have high taxes that support health programs, education, public transportation, sports, and the arts. Would you be willing to pay higher taxes to improve social services? Give reasons for your answer.

25. Do you think greater political and economic unity among the European nations is a good idea? Why or why not?

CHAPTER 23

TEST ANSWERS

Matching

1. Answer: d Objective: 31

2. Answer: e Objective: 41

3. Answer: f Objective: 21

4. Answer: c Objective: 32

5. Answer: b Objective: 11

6. Answer: i Objective: 21

7. Answer: k Objective: 11

8. Answer: g Objective: 42

9. Answer: h Objective: 31

10. Answer: l Objective: 41

Multiple Choice

11. Answer: a Objective: 41

12. Answer: a Objective: 11

13. Answer: d Objective: 12

14. Answer: b Objective: 43

15. Answer: b Objective: 22

16. Answer: a Objective: 12

17. Answer: c Objective: 11

18. Answer: b Objective: 22

19. Answer: a Objective: 31

20. Answer: c Objective: 42

Short Answer

21. Answer:
Europe has a long coastline with many ice-free harbors. Many of these harbors are located near navigable rivers, which can be used to transport goods into and from the interior. Thus, trade by sea and rivers is practical and efficient both within Europe and between Europe and other regions.

Objective: 21

22. Answer:
    An alliance is an agreement between countries to support one another against enemies.
    The two major alliances formed in Europe in the decade following World War II were the
    North Atlantic Treaty Organization (NATO), formed to provide for the common defense of
    western Europe, and the Warsaw Pact, formed by the Soviet Union and its Eastern European
    allies.

    Objective: 32

Critical Thinking

23. Answer:
    Possible answer: Among all the natural resources of Europe, water has had one of the
    greatest effects on the region's economic and political development. Western Europe's
    location along the Atlantic coast and the Mediterranean Sea enabled its countries to
    achieve political power through control of world trade beginning in the sixteenth
    century. Coastal seas are also important for fishing and are the sites of other
    resources such as oil.
        In addition, Europe's long coastline has hundreds of excellent ice-free natural
    harbors, many of which are located near the mouths of navigable rivers. These rivers
    are of great importance for trade, water resources, and hydroelectricity. Most of the
    rivers are connected by canals, which make water transportation very efficient.
    Location and an excellent water transportation network have played a key role in making
    Europe an important political and economic region.

    Objective: 21

24. Answer:
    Answers will vary. Students should provide reasons for their answers by exploring the
    benefits and drawbacks associated with higher taxes and different levels of social
    services.

    Objective: 43

25. Answer:
    Answers will vary. Some students may say that the success of the European Community
    indicates that greater unity is beneficial to all countries of the region. Other
    students may believe that increased unity might cause individual European countries to
    lose their sense of identity or alter their rich cultural heritages.

    Objective: 42

CHAPTER 24

TEST QUESTIONS

Matching

Match the term with its correct description. One term is not used.

a. Thames
b. bog
c. socialism
d. Oslo
e. constitutional monarchy
f. peat

1. Soft ground that is soaked with water

2. An economic system in which the government owns and controls the means of producing goods

3. A form of government in which a king or queen reigns but a parliament makes the laws

4. A major river that connects London with the North Sea

5. Decayed vegetable matter used as fuel in much of Ireland

Match the term with its correct description. One term is not used.

g. glaciated
h. fjord
i. uninhabitable
j. loch
k. neutral
l. geyser

6. Choosing not to take sides in international conflicts

7. A long, deep lake carved by a glacier

8. A narrow, deep inlet of the sea between high, rocky cliffs in Scandinavia

9. Unable to support human life and settlements

10. A hot spring that shoots hot water and steam into the air

Multiple Choice

Circle the letter of the <u>best</u> answer.

11. The Republic of Ireland is
    a. an independent republic that was formed in 1949.
    b. the smallest member of the United Kingdom.
    c. a former colony of Denmark.
    d. the main opponent of the Irish Republican Army.

12. Great Britain has a mild climate because of the
    a. warming effect of the geysers on the North Sea coast.
    b. mountains on the island's western coast.
    c. prevailing westerly winds blowing off the North Atlantic Drift.
    d. protected valleys formed by coastal fjords.

13. Iceland can best be described as
    a. rich in energy resources.
    b. densely forested.
    c. completely covered by an ice cap.
    d. poor and underdeveloped.

14. Britain's nationalized industries, such as its railroads,
    a. are the country's most competitive industries.
    b. are owned and operated by the government.
    c. are required to hire all applicants.
    d. receive discounts on raw materials from private suppliers.

15. Although Great Britain was the first European nation to industrialize,
    a. today it is the leader only in textile manufacturing.
    b. it never developed productive agriculture.
    c. it did not become a member of the European Community.
    d. it lost its world leadership role to foreign competition.

16. The most densely populated Nordic country is
    a. Iceland.   b. Sweden.
    c. Finland.   d. Denmark.

17. A serious problem in the Republic of Ireland is
    a. desertification due to droughts.
    b. immigration of workers from other countries.
    c. high taxes combined with high unemployment.
    d. the lack of an export market for Ireland's farm products.

18. One significant change that has taken place in the United Kingdom over the past few decades
    is that
    a. more than 50 percent of all British people are employed as agricultural workers.
    b. the British trade more with other European nations than with their distant former
       colonies.
    c. the Commonwealth of Nations has declared independence from the United Kingdom.
    d. Northern Ireland has resolved the conflicts between its Roman Catholic and Protestant
       citizens.

19. Most of Ireland's workers are employed in
    a. cattle grazing.   b. shipbuilding.
    c. manufacturing.   d. forestry.

20. Europe's leading fishing nation is
    a. Norway.   b. Finland.
    c. Germany.   d. Northern Ireland.

Short Answer

Answer the questions in the space provided.

21. What factors contributed to Britain's leadership in the Industrial Revolution?
    _____
    _____
    _____
    _____
    _____

22. How have glaciers affected the physical geography of the Nordic countries?

_____
_____
_____
_____
_____

Critical Thinking

Write your answers on a separate sheet of paper.

23. All of the Nordic countries have managed to achieve a high standard of living in spite of difficult environmental conditions. What factors do you think account for their success? Give specific examples.

24. Should Northern Ireland join the Republic of Ireland? Give reasons to support your answer.

25. About 10 percent of Sweden's industries and services are controlled by the government. What might be the advantage of a mixed economy such as this?

CHAPTER 24

TEST ANSWERS

Matching

1. Answer: b   Objective: 21

2. Answer: c   Objective: 32

3. Answer: e   Objective: 12

4. Answer: a   Objective: 11

5. Answer: f   Objective: 21

6. Answer: k   Objective: 32

7. Answer: j   Objective: 11

8. Answer: h   Objective: 31

9. Answer: i   Objective: 31

10. Answer: l   Objective: 31

Multiple Choice

11. Answer: a   Objective: 22

12. Answer: c   Objective: 11

13. Answer: a   Objective: 31

14. Answer: b   Objective: 11

15. Answer: d   Objective: 12

16. Answer: d   Objective: 32

17. Answer: c   Objective: 22

18. Answer: b   Objective: 12

19. Answer: c   Objective: 22

20. Answer: a   Objective: 32

Short Answer

21. Answer:
    Britain had extensive iron and coal resources, a large labor force, and an excellent transportation network of rivers and canals. The British also built the first railroads in the early 1800s.

    Objective: 11

22.Answer:
Glaciers carved out the fjords along the Norwegian coast. They also left glaciated plains with thin soils and thousands of lakes in Sweden and Finland. The glacial ice covering part of Iceland and Greenland contributes to making a good portion of these islands uninhabitable.

Objective: 31

Critical Thinking

23.Answer:
Factors contributing to success might include the following: an abundance of natural resources (oil in Norway, forests in Finland and Sweden, water in Iceland and Norway, mineral resources in Sweden, and fish and rich soil in Denmark); an efficient use of resources (Iceland's use of its water and geothermal resources, farming efficiency in Sweden); a neutral foreign policy (such as in Sweden where money has been spent on social programs rather than on supporting an active foreign policy); and high taxes to support social programs.

Objective: 32

24.Answer:
Answers will vary. Many years of violent unrest have probably taken their toll on Northern Ireland's economy, so the merger might not be beneficial for the Republic. Some students might argue, however, that a merger might bring peace to Northern Ireland, thus attracting more tourists, revenue, and economic development. Still, such a union would make the Protestants (currently a majority in Northern Ireland) a minority in a united Ireland. These people might lose much of the control they have over their governing.

Objective: 12

25.Answer:
Answers will vary. Students may say that a well-run mixed economy can combine the benefits of both free-market and command economies.

Objective: 32

CHAPTER 25

TEST QUESTIONS

Matching

Match the term with its correct description. One term is not used.

a. canton
b. loess
c. cosmopolitan
d. arable
e. mistral
f. foehn

1. Dust-sized soil particles deposited by the wind

2. Having many foreign influences

3. A strong, cool wind that blows from the Alps toward the Mediterranean coast

4. A Swiss state with self-governing powers

5. A warm, dry wind that blows down the slopes of the Alps

Match the term with its correct description. One term is not used.

g. polder
h. city-state
i. confederation
j. dike
k. primate city
l. nodal region

6. An urban area that ranks first in a nation in terms of population and economy

7. A lowland area that has been drained of water

8. A group of states joined together for a common purpose

9. A self-governing urban area, such as Berlin

10. A wall built to keep water out of an area

Multiple Choice

Circle the letter of the best answer.

11. Because Switzerland does not have much arable land,
    a. agriculture is limited.
    b. the nation is tectonically stable.
    c. it produces citrus fruits for export.
    d. urban areas are congested.

12. The Massif Central is a
    a. rugged Mediterranean island off the coast of France.
    b. volcanic area in south central France.
    c. mountain system that forms France's border with Spain.
    d. system of canals in central France.

13. The climate found in most of Germany is
    a. marine west coast.   b. subarctic.
    c. steppe.   d. Mediterranean.

14. Like their Swiss neighbors, Austrians
    a. produce most of the food they eat.
    b. have a variety of industries.
    c. have no energy resources.
    d. trade mostly with the United States.

15. More than half of France's electricity needs are provided by
    a. hydroelectricity.   b. tidal power.
    c. nuclear power.   d. solar power.

16. The Netherlands is unique among other European nations in that
    a. most of its people live in cosmopolitan cities.
    b. nearly one-half of the country lies below sea level.
    c. it is a confederation of 26 cantons.
    d. agriculture is more profitable than industry.

17. Germany is Europe's leading producer of
    a. steel.   b. gold.
    c. textiles.   d. natural gas.

18. France's oldest city, located on the Mediterranean coast, is
    a. Cherbourg.   b. Paris.
    c. Le Havre.   d. Marseilles.

19. Austria's capital, located on the Danube River, is
    a. Zurich.   b. Hamburg.
    c. Vienna.   d. Rotterdam.

20. The region of Flanders, where people speak Flemish, is located in
    a. Germany.   b. France.
    c. Belgium.   d. the Netherlands.

Short Answer

Answer the questions in the space provided.

21. What are Germany's five major regions? Give one characteristic of each region.
    _____
    _____
    _____
    _____
    _____

22. How was land below sea level reclaimed for farmland in the Netherlands?
    _____
    _____
    _____
    _____
    _____

Critical Thinking

Write your answers on a separate sheet of paper.

23. Imagine you are in an airplane flying over West Central Europe. Describe how the physical setting beneath you changes as you travel from southern France northeast over Belgium and the Netherlands to northern Germany.

24. How might Switzerland's economy be affected if it joined the United Nations or NATO?

25. Which of Germany's regions has the most economic importance to the country? Explain.

CHAPTER 25

TEST ANSWERS

Matching

1. Answer: b Objective: 22

2. Answer: c Objective: 32

3. Answer: e Objective: 11

4. Answer: a Objective: 41

5. Answer: f Objective: 41

6. Answer: k Objective: 12

7. Answer: g Objective: 31

8. Answer: i Objective: 41

9. Answer: h Objective: 22

10. Answer: j Objective: 31

Multiple Choice

11. Answer: a Objective: 41

12. Answer: b Objective: 11

13. Answer: a Objective: 21

14. Answer: b Objective: 42

15. Answer: c Objective: 11

16. Answer: b Objective: 31

17. Answer: a Objective: 11

18. Answer: d Objective: 12

19. Answer: c Objective: 42

20. Answer: c Objective: 32

Short Answer

21. Answer:
    Germany's five major regions are Northwestern Germany, the Ruhr, the Rhineland, Southern Germany, and the former East Germany. Characteristics given will vary but may concern each region's physical, economic, historical, or urban geography.

    Objective: 22

22. Answer:

First, dikes were built to keep out water. Then a system of canals was constructed to remove the water. The land was eventually drained, or pumped dry, by windmills.

Objective: 31

Critical Thinking

23. Answer:

Possible answer: Starting in southern France, the rugged landscape of the Pyrenees would give way to the hilly Central Uplands region of central France. Then the plane would fly over the productive lowlands agricultural region of the Northern European Plain in northern France. When passing over Belgium, the forested hills of the Ardennes as well as coastal regions might be visible. Over both Belgium and the Netherlands, the plane would fly above coastal plains, many of which have been reclaimed from the sea. Passing into northern Germany, the dominant landform would be the North German Plain, which is part of the Northern European Plain. The plane would pass over several major rivers during the course of the flight.

Objective: 11

24. Answer:

Possible answer: Some students might argue that Switzerland's neutrality and stability is what makes it attractive to foreign investors. Joining the UN or NATO might have a negative effect on its economy by discouraging investment.

Objective: 41

25. Answer:

Possible answer: Some students might view the regions with the greatest variety of resources and industries, such as southern Germany, to be the most valuable. Others might view the regions that have rich coal deposits and heavy concentrations of industry, such as the Ruhr region, as being most important. Students are unlikely to say eastern Germany, which trails behind the rest of the country in transportation and industry.

Objective: 22

CHAPTER 26

TEST QUESTIONS

Matching

Match the term with its correct description. One term is not used.

a. autonomy
b. Meseta
c. Gibraltar
d. dictatorship
e. cork
f. Renaissance

1. A bark stripped from the trunk of the Mediterranean oak

2. A territory of the United Kingdom, located where the Mediterranean Sea meets the Atlantic Ocean at the southern tip of the Iberian Peninsula

3. A high plateau in Spain that is almost completely surrounded by mountains

4. A historical period during which a renewed interest in learning spread throughout Europe

5. The right to self-government

Match the term with its correct description. One term is not used.

g. coalition
h. balance of trade
i. Strait of Messina
j. plaza
k. dialect
l. Isthmus of Corinth

6. A type of government in which several political parties work together to run the country

7. A public square in the center of a Spanish town

8. The relationship between the value of a country's exports and imports

9. A regional variety of a major language

10. The body of water that separates the island of Sicily from the Italian peninsula

Multiple Choice

Circle the letter of the best answer.

11. Italy's Po Valley is a region that is
    a. agricultural but not industrial.
    b. industrial but not agricultural.
    c. both agricultural and industrial.
    d. undeveloped.

12. Greece's landforms are mainly
    a. rolling hills and wide plains.
    b. high volcanic plateaus.
    c. peninsulas, islands, and mountains.
    d. coastal lowlands and deep, wide valleys.

13. The most populated areas of Spain are located
    a. on the coastal plains and in river valleys.
    b. in the semiarid steppe climate region.
    c. in the Cantabrian Mountains.
    d. near the border with Portugal.

14. Greece's most populated region, where the city of Athens is located, is
    a. central Greece.   b. Crete.
    c. northern Greece.   d. the Peloponnesus.

15. A person studying the art and architecture of the Renaissance would probably be most
    interested in visiting
    a. Florence.   b. Athens.   c. Lisbon.   d. Madrid.

16. Italy's economic heartland is
    a. the Po Valley.   b. Vatican City.
    c. the island of Sicily.   d. Sardinia.

17. Portugal's two largest cities are
    a. Valencia and Tagus.   b. Madrid and Barcelona.
    c. Douro and Euskara.   d. Oporto and Lisbon.

18. As a result of the occupation of Spain by the Moors,
    a. Muslim influences are still visible in Spain today.
    b. Spain became more active in establishing overseas colonies.
    c. Spain and Portugal became military allies.
    d. most Spanish people today speak Arabic.

19. Southern Italy differs from central Italy in that it is
    a. where most of the nation's industrial cities are located.
    b. the "breadbasket" of Italy.
    c. a poor, underdeveloped region with an arid climate.
    d. the site of most ancient Roman ruins.

20. The European microstate that borders both Switzerland and Austria is
    a. Vatican City.   b. Liechtenstein.
    c. Monaco.   d. Andorra.

Short Answer

Answer the questions in the space provided.

21. What are some of the problems associated with Spain's tourist industry?
    _____
    _____
    _____
    _____
    _____

22. What factors prevented Italy from becoming unified until the late nineteenth century?
    _____
    _____
    _____
    _____
    _____

176

Critical Thinking

Write your answers on a separate sheet of paper.

23. What physical and political factors have caused Greece and southern Italy to be less economically developed than other regions and nations in the European Community?

24. Do you think Spain should grant independence to the Basques? Why might it hesitate about doing so?

25. If you could spend only three days in Italy, which part of the country would you prefer to visit? Explain your choice.

CHAPTER 26

TEST ANSWERS

Matching

   1.Answer: e Objective: 12

   2.Answer: c Objective: 32

   3.Answer: b Objective: 11

   4.Answer: f Objective: 21

   5.Answer: a Objective: 13

   6.Answer: g Objective: 21

   7.Answer: j Objective: 13

   8.Answer: h Objective: 21

   9.Answer: k Objective: 13

   10.Answer: i Objective: 21

Multiple Choice

   11.Answer: c Objective: 22

   12.Answer: c Objective: 31

   13.Answer: a Objective: 11

   14.Answer: a Objective: 31

   15.Answer: a Objective: 21

   16.Answer: a Objective: 22

   17.Answer: d Objective: 12

   18.Answer: a Objective: 13

   19.Answer: c Objective: 22

   20.Answer: b Objective: 32

Short Answer

   21.Answer:
   A construction boom along the Mediterranean coast and in the Canary Islands has caused pollution and overcrowding, and some scenery is blocked by high-rise buildings. The tourist industry also competes with agriculture for water, a limited resource in the region.

   Objective: 12

22. Answer:

Rivalry among city-states such as Florence, Venice, and Genoa, and invasions by outside powers such as Spain and Austria prevented Italy from becoming unified until the late nineteenth century.

Objective: 21

Critical Thinking

23. Answer:

Possible answer: Similar physical and political factors have caused Greece and southern Italy to develop more slowly. Both regions suffer from a lack of natural resources. Southern Italy has extremely dry summers, and its southern islands are mountainous and rocky. These conditions make farming difficult. Greece, too, has a dry climate and mountainous terrain, with a limited supply of flat land and water for farming. Rugged terrain and the presence of so many islands may also hinder transportation in Greece and southern Italy, thereby discouraging industrialization, which relies on good transportation to bring in resources and carry out finished products. Furthermore, both regions have experienced unstable political conditions, which may have contributed to the relative lack of development.

Objective: 31

24. Answer:

Answers will vary. Some students may say that the Basques, who speak their own language and have a distinct culture, have the right to form an independent nation. Although they have autonomy, they are not completely self-governing. One reason Spain might hesitate about granting independence has to do with the Basques' location in the Pyrenees and along the Bay of Biscay. Spain would lose control of part of its border with France if it granted independence to the Basques.

Objective: 13

25. Answer:

Answers will vary. Students should give reasons for their choices. Students choosing central Italy might express a desire to see the ruins in Rome and/or Renaissance art and architecture in Florence. Students choosing northern Italy might be interested in the Alps or in Venice. Southern Italy might be selected for Capri, Mount Vesuvius, and Pompeii.

Objective: 22

CHAPTER 27

TEST QUESTIONS

Matching

Match the term with its correct description. One term is not used.

a. Carpathian Mountains
b. legacy
c. Dinaric Alps
d. complementary regions
e. nationalism
f. regional specialization

1. Something received from a previous era

2. Two regions, such as the Czech and Slovak territories in 1918, that benefit from being merged with each other

3. A mountain range on the Balkan Peninsula that extends inland from the Adriatic Sea

4. A mountain range that stretches from the Czech Republic to Romania

5. A plan under which each country in a region produces goods that it can make or grow best or for which it has the best resources

Match the term with its correct description. One term is not used.

g. Prague
h. Ploiesti
i. Solidarity
j. COMECON
k. NATO
l. Slovenia

6. The capital of the Czech Republic, where one of Europe's oldest universities is located

7. The organization that oversaw economic ties between the Soviet Union and Eastern Europe

8. The location of Romania's rich oil fields

9. An independent organization of Polish workers, formed in 1980, that resisted the authority of the Communist party

10. One of the new countries of the former Yugoslavia

Multiple Choice

Circle the letter of the best answer.

11. To become more economically developed, Romania would probably find it helpful to
    a. become a member of COMECON.
    b. develop its mineral resources.
    c. merge its economy with that of Albania.
    d. create state-controlled, cooperative farms.

12. The climate in the northern part of Eastern Europe is
    a. humid continental.   b. steppe.
    c. Mediterranean.   d. tundra.

13. Between World War I and World War II, the countries of Eastern Europe
    a. were settled by waves of invaders.
    b. were controlled by the Austrian and Turkish empires.
    c. enjoyed independence from foreign control.
    d. were ethnically uniform.

14. All of the following are capital cities in Eastern Europe except
    a. Warsaw.   b. Budapest.   c. Ploiesti.   d. Sofia.

15. Tension among ethnic groups in Eastern Europe has often resulted from
    a. different languages and religions.
    b. the region's isolation from the rest of Europe.
    c. trade disputes.
    d. arguments over Soviet control.

16. The strong central government weakened and civil war began in the former Yugoslavia as a result of
    a. the adoption of Roman Catholicism as the official state religion.
    b. conflict between the regions of Macedonia and Serbia.
    c. the destruction of Sarajevo by Serbian forces.
    d. Josef Broz Tito's death and the end of communism in the Soviet Union.

17. In 1989, Poland became the first Eastern European country to
    a. resolve conflicts among competing ethnic groups.
    b. begin cleaning up its polluted environment.
    c. establish a government independent from Soviet control.
    d. develop a Communist-controlled economy.

18. Both the Czech Republic and Hungary
    a. have made rapid progress toward free-market economies.
    b. lack the resources necessary for economic prosperity.
    c. remain politically repressive.
    d. have many mineral resources but little fertile land.

19. Since the breakup of the Soviet Union, nearly all Eastern European countries have
    a. experienced some degree of financial distress.
    b. become more involved in the Warsaw Pact.
    c. adopted Communist governments and command economies.
    d. cooperated in establishing the "Iron Curtain" between Russia and Eastern Europe.

20. A belief of many radical Serbs that has fueled the conflict in the former Yugoslavia is that
    a. Bosnian Muslims should be allowed to live only in Croatia.
    b. no Serb should be governed by someone from another ethnic group.
    c. Croats and Bosnians should live in Serbia.
    d. a command economy should be established to restore order to the region.

Short Answer

Answer the questions in the space provided.

21. What are the five new countries that have formed out of the former Yugoslavia? In which two countries has there been the least conflict since the breakup? What enabled these countries to avoid most of the conflict?

_____
_____
_____
_____
_____

22. Why does Eastern Europe contain so many ethnic groups?

_____
_____
_____
_____
_____

Critical Thinking

Write your answers on a separate sheet of paper.

23. Which country of Eastern Europe do you think is best prepared for the challenges of a free-market economy? Explain your answer by comparing and contrasting that country's political, economic, and social characteristics with those of other Eastern European countries.

24. Should the governments of western European countries help Eastern Europeans solve their environmental problems? Why or why not?

25. What solutions can you propose for the ongoing conflict in the former Yugoslavia?

CHAPTER 27

TEST ANSWERS

Matching

1.Answer: b Objective: 12

2.Answer: d Objective: 21

3.Answer: c Objective: 11

4.Answer: a Objective: 11

5.Answer: f Objective: 12

6.Answer: g Objective: 22

7.Answer: j Objective: 12

8.Answer: h Objective: 21

9.Answer: i Objective: 22

10.Answer: l Objective: 31

Multiple Choice

11.Answer: b Objective: 21

12.Answer: a Objective: 11

13.Answer: c Objective: 11

14.Answer: c Objective: 22

15.Answer: a Objective: 11

16.Answer: d Objective: 31

17.Answer: c Objective: 12

18.Answer: a Objective: 21

19.Answer: a Objective: 12

20.Answer: b Objective: 32

Short Answer

21.Answer:
The five new countries are Serbia and Montenegro (which together have claimed the name Yugoslavia), Bosnia and Herzegovina, Croatia, Slovenia, and Macedonia. Slovenia and Macedonia have experienced the least conflict—in Slovenia because there are few ethnic minorities and in Macedonia because Macedonians and Serbs have a history of cooperation.

Objective: 31

22. Answer:

Eastern Europe has been a cultural crossroads for migrating peoples for centuries. These immigrants have brought with them their own languages, religions, and other culture traits. In some areas, mountains have hindered communication among and isolated the different groups, further enabling the survival of distinct cultures.

Objective: 11

Critical Thinking

23. Answer:

Answers will vary. Hungary, Poland, the Czech Republic, and Bulgaria are the most industrialized nations of Eastern Europe and, therefore, may be the best prepared to handle a market economy. Some students may say that Hungary's future seems the most promising, since it is making strong economic links with western Europe and the United States.

Poland, meanwhile, is attempting to model its economy after the developed countries of Europe. The Czech Republic is embracing a free-market economy more enthusiastically than Slovakia, which is more rural. Romania has the potential to be a developed country, with oil resources and other mineral resources as well. In Bulgaria, the new government contains many leaders from the Communist era, but a market economy is growing slowly. The country was also more prosperous under the Soviet Union, an advantage the country might be able to retain.

Albania is the least likely to develop a market economy before other countries of Eastern Europe, as it is physically, culturally, and economically isolated from other countries of the region. The country recently voted to become Communist again.

Objective: 21

24. Answer:

Answers will vary. Some students might say that western Europe would benefit, in the long run, by spending money and investing labor in helping clean up pollution in Eastern Europe, as there are no borders in the air or the water. Other students, however, may say that the countries of western Europe have their own environmental problems to solve and that these should take precedence over the problems of other regions.

Objective: 12

25. Answer:

Answers will vary. Students might consider options such as outside military intervention, from NATO or the United Nations, or mediation and negotiation. They should acknowledge that the situation is complex and difficult to resolve, largely because the tensions between ethnic groups are long-standing and persistent.

Objective: 32

UNIT 5

TEST QUESTIONS

Matching

Match the term with its correct description. One term is not used.

a. Warsaw Pact
b. Carpathian Mountains
c. Pyrenees
d. COMECON
e. Po Valley
f. European Community (EC)

1. The mountain range that separates France from Spain

2. An organization formed in 1957 to break down trade barriers among European nations

3. A prosperous region of northern Italy, where much of the nation's industry and agriculture is located

4. A military alliance formed between the Soviet Union and countries of Eastern Europe after World War II

5. A mountain range in Eastern Europe

Match the term with its correct description. One term is not used.

g. Ruhr
h. geyser
i. Ardennes
j. polder
k. loch
l. Croatia

6. A long, deep lake carved by a glacier

7. A lowland area that has been drained of water

8. A hot spring that shoots hot water and steam into the air

9. One of the new countries of the former Yugoslavia

10. A German region that is heavily industrialized

Multiple Choice

Circle the letter of the <u>best</u> answer.

11. Peninsulas make up most of the countries of
    a. Italy and Denmark.
    b. Poland and France.
    c. Ireland and Great Britain.
    d. Austria and the Czech Republic.

12. Most of Europe has a mild climate because of the
    a. warm breezes from the Mediterranean Sea.
    b. high elevation of much of the continent.
    c. moderating influence of the North Atlantic Ocean.
    d. orographic effect along the western coast.

13. In the history of Europe, the event that took place most recently was the
    a. reunification of Germany.   b. Second World War.
    c. Moors' occupation of Spain.   d. formation of COMECON.

14. Unlike many other European nations, neither Sweden nor Switzerland
    a. has a large urban population.
    b. has a prosperous economy.
    c. takes sides in international conflicts.
    d. provides its people with many social programs.

15. The British Commonwealth of Nations and the French Community are both
    a. military alliances in western Europe.
    b. European branches of the United Nations.
    c. internal security organizations.
    d. organizations that preserve ties between European nations and their former colonies.

16. The countries that share a border with Spain are
    a. Belgium and Germany.   b. Portugal and France.
    c. France and the Netherlands.   d. Switzerland and Austria.

17. The military alliance formed in 1949 for the common defense of western Europe against
    Soviet aggression was the
    a. Warsaw Pact.
    b. European Community (EC).
    c. North Atlantic Treaty Organization (NATO).
    d. United Nations (UN).

18. The Alps are important to Switzerland and Austria because they form the basis of the
    countries'
    a. banking industry.   b. steel industry.
    c. agricultural industry.   d. tourist industry.

19. The most recent event that had the greatest impact on the economies of Eastern European
    countries was the
    a. formation of the European Community (EC).
    b. election of Josef Broz Tito in Yugoslavia.
    c. breakup of the Soviet Union.
    d. adoption of socialist policies in Sweden.

20. Northern Ireland and the former Yugoslavia region are similar in that they both
    a. have mild, humid-continental climates.
    b. are members of the European Community.
    c. are located on the Northern European Plain.
    d. suffer from violent cultural conflicts.

Short Answer

Answer the questions in the space provided.

21. What changes took place in Europe as a result of the Industrial Revolution?
    _____
    _____
    _____
    _____
    _____

22. List Europe's four major landform regions.

_____
_____
_____
_____
_____
_____

Critical Thinking

Write your answers on a separate sheet of paper.

23. Based on what you have learned about Europe's history and economy, what predictions can you make about what the region might be like in the year 2025? Support your predictions with examples from the unit.

24. Why do you think large areas of low population density are found in the northern half of the Scandinavian region?

25. How is the ancient history of Italy and Greece one of the most important economic resources of these countries?

UNIT 5

TEST ANSWERS

Matching

   1.Answer: c Objective: 51

   2.Answer: f Objective: 56

   3.Answer: e Objective: 53

   4.Answer: a Objective: 56

   5.Answer: b Objective: 51

   6.Answer: k Objective: 51

   7.Answer: j Objective: 53

   8.Answer: h Objective: 53

   9.Answer: l Objective: 52

  10.Answer: g Objective: 53

Multiple Choice

  11.Answer: a Objective: 51

  12.Answer: c Objective: 51

  13.Answer: a Objective: 52

  14.Answer: c Objective: 56

  15.Answer: d Objective: 55

  16.Answer: b Objective: 51

  17.Answer: c Objective: 56

  18.Answer: d Objective: 53

  19.Answer: c Objective: 52

  20.Answer: d Objective: 54

Short Answer

21.Answer:

The Industrial Revolution increased trade and living standards. Natural resources such as coal and iron were developed, and complex transportation networks based on railroads and steel ships were established. Farmers took jobs in the cities, which grew dramatically during the nineteenth century.

Objective: 53

22. Answer:
Europe's four major landform regions are the Northwest Highlands, the Northern European Plain, the Central Uplands, and the Alpine mountain system.

Objective: 51

Critical Thinking

23. Answer:
Answers will vary. Some students may predict that Europe as a whole will be prosperous—that it will have resolved its ethnic conflicts, maintained a good standard of living, and further developed renewable energy resources. Others may predict that the continent will be increasingly polarized into a prosperous north and a poorer south. They may also predict that the economies of Eastern European countries will continue to trail those of western Europe, and that conflicts in Northern Ireland, the former Yugoslavia, and elsewhere may flare up again. Students may also address whether Europe will remain a powerful force in the global community; whether European countries will continue to develop economically and maintain stable, democratic governments; and whether the region as a whole will experience increasing unity or disunity.

Objective: 53

24. Answer:
Possible answer: Few people live in the northern half of the Scandinavian region because of the climate conditions and terrain. The extreme subarctic climate found across northern Norway, Sweden, and Finland gives the area long, cold winters and short summers. Also, the rocky, rugged terrain with poorly drained valleys supports little economic activity. Some students might also suggest that the uneven patterns of light caused by the region's high latitude—constant darkness in winter and constant daylight in summer—may discourage permanent settlement.

Objective: 51

25. Answer:
Possible answer: Millions of tourists visit Italy and Greece each year to see the ruins, such as the Forum, the Colosseum, and the Parthenon, of each country's ancient civilizations. The tourist industry, and thus each country's ancient history, is vital to the economies of both countries.

Objective: 52

CHAPTER 28

TEST QUESTIONS

Matching

Match the term with its correct description. One term is not used.

a. *glasnost*
b. totalitarian
c. abdicate
d. czar
e. autarky
f. *perestroika*

1. To resign from a position of power, as Russia's leader did in early 1917

2. The Soviet policy promoted in the late 1980s to allow for more open discussion of the country's problems

3. A policy, followed by Soviet planners, of striving for self-sufficiency in economic production

4. A monarch of the Russian Empire

5. The Soviet policy promoted in the late 1980s of major economic reforms

Match the term with its correct description. One term is not used.

g. client state
h. Boris Yeltsin
i. Karl Marx
j. superpower
k. Mikhail Gorbachev
l. soviet

6. A Soviet leader who promoted openness and economic restructuring

7. A nineteenth-century German philosopher whose ideas about the exploitation of the working classes formed the basis for the Soviet Union's early economic policies

8. The first democratically elected president of Russia

9. A country that is politically, economically, or militarily dependent on a more powerful country

10. The local governing council of each republic in the USSR

Multiple Choice

Circle the letter of the best answer.

11. Russia's expansion into European territory was hindered by all of the following except
    a. differences between Russian and European ideas of government and political control.
    b. the Ottoman Empire and the powerful kingdoms of Sweden and Poland.
    c. differences between the religions of Russia and Europe.
    d. the large numbers of non-Russian peoples within Russia.

12. Orthodox Christianity was brought to Russia by
    a. immigrants from the steppe.
    b. Viking traders from Scandinavia.
    c. missionaries from the Balkans.
    d. Mongol invaders.

13. The Soviet Union was importing large amounts of grain by the late 1950s because
    a. the goal of autarky had been achieved.
    b. the country's economy was geared toward producing consumer goods.
    c. the price of grain on world markets had never been lower.
    d. food production on government-run farms was inadequate.

14. The Communist Revolution occurred when
    a. V. I. Lenin and the Bolsheviks overthrew the government in 1917.
    b. Ivan the Terrible assumed power in Russia in 1547.
    c. The Soviet Union broke apart in 1991.
    d. Joseph Stalin took power in 1924.

15. All of the following increased or improved under Communist rule except
    a. personal freedoms.   b. industry.
    c. education.   d. health care.

16. An important Russian trading center that emerged in the ninth century was
    a. Novosibirsk.   b. Kiev.
    c. Siberia.   d. Ukraine.

17. A policy of major economic reforms, called *perestroika,* began under the leadership of
    a. Mikhail Gorbachev.   b. Catherine the Great.
    c. Karl Marx.   d. Genghis Khan.

18. Under Stalin's five-year plans,
    a. the government invested heavily in agriculture.
    b. farmers were not allowed to grow crops in private plots.
    c. Russia experienced dramatic industrial growth.
    d. all power was vested in the republics' soviets.

19. One result of the central Soviet government's loss of authority in the late 1980s was that
    a. Boris Yeltsin was forced to abdicate.
    b. Eastern European client states collapsed.
    c. order, stability, and security increased.
    d. Russia became economically self-sufficient.

20. One troubling consequence of the breakup of the Soviet Union has been the
    a. adoption of traditional five-year plans.
    b. renewal of Cold War hostilities.
    c. increase in ethnic tensions.
    d. decrease in religious worship.

Short Answer

Answer the questions in the space provided.

21. What environmental challenges does the former Soviet Union face today?

_____
_____
_____
_____
_____

22. Give two examples of how personal freedoms were limited in the Soviet Union.

_____
_____
_____
_____
_____

Critical Thinking

Write your answers on a separate sheet of paper.

23. Describe the key economic and political principles on which the Soviet Union was based. Were these principles reflected in reality?

24. Would you prefer to have lived in Russia in the 1890s or in the 1950s? Give reasons for your answer.

25. What position do you think a government committed to a policy of autarky would take on trade with other countries?

CHAPTER 28

TEST ANSWERS

Matching

   1.Answer: c Objective: 12

   2.Answer: a Objective: 31

   3.Answer: e Objective: 21

   4.Answer: d Objective: 11

   5.Answer: f Objective: 31

   6.Answer: k Objective: 31

   7.Answer: i Objective: 21

   8.Answer: h Objective: 31

   9.Answer: g Objective: 23

  10.Answer: l Objective: 21

Multiple Choice

  11.Answer: d Objective: 11

  12.Answer: c Objective: 11

  13.Answer: d Objective: 21

  14.Answer: a Objective: 12

  15.Answer: a Objective: 22

  16.Answer: b Objective: 11

  17.Answer: a Objective: 31

  18.Answer: c Objective: 21

  19.Answer: b Objective: 23

  20.Answer: c Objective: 32

Short Answer

  21.Answer:
    Deforestation, river and lake pollution, and the improper disposal of toxic wastes are some of the region's environmental challenges.

    Objective: 32

22.Answer:
People who disagreed with the government could be jailed. Also, Soviet leaders attempted to eliminate religious worship, which they believed competed with devotion to communism.

Objective: 22

Critical Thinking

23.Answer:
The economic principles on which the Soviet Union was founded in 1917 were based on the views of Karl Marx, a nineteenth-century German philosopher. Marx believed that capitalist business leaders took advantage of their workers, keeping the workers poor to maintain their own power and wealth. The first Soviet leader, V. I. Lenin, thought that government, rather than private, ownership of all farms and factories would benefit the most people. In actuality, however, government control of the economy caused many problems, including low food production, low efficiency, low product quality, and poor working conditions.
    Politically, the Soviet Union was divided into a number of republics founded on the idea that each of the country's large ethnic groups should have its own territory. However, because Communist party leaders in Moscow made all decisions for the country, the republics had little real power. Also, under Lenin's, and later Stalin's, rule, the government tried to promote a single culture. Nonetheless, the languages, cultures, and religions of various ethnic groups survived.

Objective: 21

24.Answer:
Answers will vary. Students should compare the living conditions of the two decades. They should note that life in both decades was difficult. For example, in the 1890s, most of the people were poor peasants, and food shortages made conditions even worse. In the 1950s, although life was as good as it had ever been for many people, food shortages still existed, working conditions were poor, housing was cramped, and personal freedoms were severely restricted.

Objective: 12

25.Answer:
Because autarky is a policy of economic self-sufficiency, such a government would try to limit imports as much as possible. Exports might be encouraged so long as the country did not become overly dependent on the money made from those exports.

Objective: 21

CHAPTER 29

TEST QUESTIONS

Matching

Match the term with its correct description. One term is not used.

a. Western Siberian Lowland
b. heavy industry
c. smelter
d. Russian Plain
e. light industry
f. serf

1. The region where most of the Russian people live

2. A peasant bound to the land

3. A factory that processes ores such as copper and iron

4. Manufacturing based on metals such as steel

5. The production of goods such as clothing

Match the term with its correct description. One term is not used.

g. permafrost
h. Kuznetsk Basin
i. taiga
j. Kamchatka Peninsula
k. habitation fog
l. Central Siberian Plateau

6. Siberia's most important industrial region, where rich coal deposits are located

7. An atmospheric condition caused by fumes and smoke from cities

8. A region of upland plains and valleys with many undeveloped mineral resources

9. A large forest of tall, evergreen needle-leaf trees

10. A region in the Russian Far East where small oil and gas fields are located

Multiple Choice

Circle the letter of the best answer.

11. Siberia's most important economic activities are
    a. textile production and oil refining.
    b. high technology and fishing.
    c. farming and cattle raising.
    d. lumbering and mining.

12. Russia has enormous reserves of all of the following except
   a. oil.   b. forests.   c. silver.   d. coal.

13. Russia's agricultural potential is limited by
   a. a shortage of farmers.   b. the country's climate.
   c. much swampland.   d. agribusiness.

14. The chief seaport of the Russian Far East is
   a. Moscow.   b. Vladivostok.
   c. Gorky.   d. Novosibirsk.

15. Few consumer goods are produced in Russia because
   a. many of these goods can be inexpensively imported from other countries.
   b. demand for these goods is very low.
   c. industry has concentrated on producing military goods.
   d. the country has never become industrialized.

16. The Congress of People's Deputies is
   a. the legislature of the Russian Federation.
   b. an association of farmers in collective farms.
   c. an association of law enforcement officials.
   d. the cabinet of advisors to the president of the Russian Federation.

17. A heavily industrialized region with rich mineral deposits is
   a. Siberia.   b. the Urals region.
   c. the Russian Far East.   d. the St. Petersburg region.

18. One reason that economic progress has been slow since the breakup of the Soviet Union is that
   a. the government has not promoted privatization of farms and businesses.
   b. Russia has limited resources and industrial potential.
   c. most Russians are poorly educated.
   d. there are few well-trained business managers in Russia.

19. Most settlement in Siberia is located
   a. along the route of the Trans-Siberian Railroad.
   b. on the Kamchatka Peninsula.
   c. between St. Petersburg and Moscow.
   d. around Lake Baykal.

20. One economic change that Russia is undergoing is the
   a. diversification of companies that have focused on one product.
   b. establishment of state and collective farms.
   c. creation of monopolies in order to encourage competition.
   d. increased production of military goods.

Short Answer

Answer the questions in the space provided.

21. How did the Communist government attempt to modernize agriculture in the 1920s and 1930s?

   _____
   _____
   _____
   _____
   _____

22. What is the Baykal-Amur Mainline (BAM)? Why was it built?

_____
_____
_____
_____
_____

Critical Thinking

Write your answers on a separate sheet of paper.

23. Describe the political and cultural characteristics of the Russian Federation.

24. Do you think that Siberia might one day be as populous and developed as the Moscow, St. Petersburg, Volga, or Urals regions? Why or why not?

25. Russians have more freedom today, but there is less security than in the past. Which would you prefer—reliable, though limiting, security or an exciting but uncertain present and future? Why?

CHAPTER 29

TEST ANSWERS

Matching

1.Answer: d Objective: 11

2.Answer: f Objective: 22

3.Answer: c Objective: 32

4.Answer: b Objective: 32

5.Answer: e Objective: 32

6.Answer: h Objective: 32

7.Answer: k Objective: 12

8.Answer: l Objective: 11

9.Answer: i Objective: 12

10.Answer: j Objective: 32

Multiple Choice

11.Answer: d Objective: 32

12.Answer: c Objective: 21

13.Answer: b Objective: 22

14.Answer: b Objective: 32

15.Answer: c Objective: 31

16.Answer: a Objective: 41

17.Answer: b Objective: 32

18.Answer: d Objective: 42

19.Answer: a Objective: 32

20.Answer: a Objective: 31

Short Answer

21.Answer:
The government seized all private farmlands and formed collective and state farms. On collective farms, workers were to share profits. State farms were run like factories in that workers received a salary.

Objective: 22

22.Answer:
The Baykal-Amur Mainline is a railway that was completed across eastern Siberia in 1989. It was built so that resources from Siberia could be more easily transported to other areas in Russia.

Objective: 32

Critical Thinking

23.Answer:
Possible answer: The Russian Federation, formed after the breakup of the Soviet Union, is still taking shape. The government has a president and a legislature called the Congress of People's deputies. The latter elects the Supreme Soviet, a smaller body, which governs on a daily basis. The division of power between the president and the legislature is still unclear.

Russia is a diverse country with many ethnic groups. At one time, ethnic groups lived within territorial subdivisions that were tightly controlled by Moscow. Today, 20 republics, with their own legislatures and leaders, make up about 15 percent of Russia's territory. Of these, the most populous is Bashkortostan. The largest territory is Yakutia-Sakha in Siberia, and the most assertive republic is Tatarstan, which has declared its full independence. Although the republics supposedly were created as representations of ethnic group membership, ethnic Russians form a majority of the population in many of the republics.

Objective: 41

24.Answer:
Answers will vary. Most students will probably say that because of its harsh climate, terrain, and distance from Russia's more developed regions, Siberia will never be as fully developed as these regions. The climate restricts agriculture, transportation, and other economic activities. Even if Siberia's vast resources were fully developed, few people would probably be drawn to live there.

Objective: 32

25.Answer:
Answers will vary. Some students may try to identify with the Russian people, who have experienced the trade-off of security for freedom. Students should provide reasons to support their choice.

Objective: 42

CHAPTER 30

TEST QUESTIONS

Matching

Match the term with its correct description. One term is not used.

a. Caucasus
b. Georgia
c. Cossacks
d. White Russians
e. Donets Basin
f. Baku

1. A group of people who controlled Ukraine's steppe region beginning in the sixteenth century and fought the southward expansion of the Russian Empire

2. A region in Ukraine where productive coal fields are found

3. The capital of Azerbaijan and the center of a large oil-refining industry

4. The region of mountains and valleys that separates the Black Sea and the Caspian Sea

5. A country that has experienced violent unrest among its ethnic groups since independence

Match the term with its correct description. One term is not used.

g. collective
h. Minsk
i. homogeneous
j. deciduous
k. Odesa
l. Crimea

6. The capital of Belarus and the country's major industrial and transportation center

7. The Black Sea's busiest port, located in Ukraine

8. Of the same kind, as in ethnic composition

9. A region of Ukraine where vineyards, fruit orchards, and warm beaches are found

10. A type of inefficient farm still found in Ukraine today

Multiple Choice

Circle the letter of the best answer.

11. Ukraine's major resources are
    a. mineral deposits and rich farmland.
    b. oil and natural-gas deposits.
    c. forests and fish.
    d. geothermal energy and a complex network of waterways.

12. Belarus's economy has, for the most part, relied on
    a. agriculture and food processing.
    b. education and technical training.
    c. military production.
    d. state and collective farms.

13. The city of Kyyiv is the
    a. site where the Russian royal family built summer palaces.
    b. industrial center of Armenia and home to the country's Jewish population.
    c. capital of Ukraine as well as its cultural and historical center.
    d. center of Azerbaijan's oil-refining industry.

14. Donets'k, Kharkiv, and Odesa are
    a. the capitals of Belarus, Ukraine, and Armenia.
    b. dams built along the Dnipro River.
    c. ethnic groups found in the Caucasus.
    d. important cities in Ukraine.

15. Armenia differs from other countries of the Caucasus in that
    a. it lies in the rain shadow of the Carpathian Mountains.
    b. pollution resulting from industrialization is a serious problem.
    c. most of the region's oil is produced here.
    d. most of its people are ethnically similar and practice the same religion.

16. Belarus resembles the Soviet Union of the 1970s in that
    a. it has a planned economy with few freedoms.
    b. consumer goods are widely available.
    c. more people are Jews than Eastern Orthodox Christians.
    d. it has a free-market economy.

17. The number of ethnic groups in the Caucasus is directly related to the region's
    a. climate conditions.
    b. landforms.
    c. relationship with the Soviet Union.
    d. uneven distribution of resources.

18. A country that has strong ties to Iran and Islam is
    a. Belarus.   b. Georgia.
    c. Armenia.   d. Azerbaijan.

19. Armenia and Azerbaijan are in conflict about
    a. the status of Crimea.
    b. the status of Nagorno-Karabakh.
    c. tariffs and other trade issues.
    d. promoting tourism in the Caucasus.

20. A country that shares physical and cultural features with Poland is
    a. Belarus.   b. Azerbaijan.   c. Crimea.   d. Armenia.

Short Answer

Answer the questions in the space provided.

21. How has Ukraine's physical geography changed as a result of human settlement?
    _____
    _____
    _____
    _____
    _____

22. Describe the three landform regions of the Caucasus.

_____

_____

_____

_____

_____

Critical Thinking

Write your answers on a separate sheet of paper.

23. What effect has independence had on the economies of Ukraine, Belarus, and the Caucasus countries?

24. Which of the countries discussed in this chapter do you think will be most prosperous 20 years from now? Why?

25. Who do you believe should control Crimea—Russia or Ukraine? Or do you think Crimea should become an independent country? Why?

CHAPTER 30

TEST ANSWERS

Matching

1.Answer: c Objective: 12

2.Answer: e Objective: 11

3.Answer: f Objective: 31

4.Answer: a Objective: 31

5.Answer: b Objective: 32

6.Answer: h Objective: 21

7.Answer: k Objective: 11

8.Answer: i Objective: 32

9.Answer: l Objective: 11

10.Answer: g Objective: 11

Multiple Choice

11.Answer: a Objective: 11

12.Answer: b Objective: 21

13.Answer: c Objective: 12

14.Answer: d Objective: 11

15.Answer: d Objective: 32

16.Answer: a Objective: 21

17.Answer: b Objective: 32

18.Answer: d Objective: 32

19.Answer: b Objective: 32

20.Answer: a Objective: 22

Short Answer

21.Answer:
Ukraine was once covered with deciduous forests in the north and steppe grasslands in the south. Today, most of Ukraine's lands are covered by farm fields, and little of the original vegetation remains.

Objective: 11

22. Answer:

The three landform regions of the Caucasus include a wide mountain range in the north, lowlands along the Black and Caspian seas, and a rugged, volcanic plateau in the south.

Objective: 31

Critical Thinking

23. Answer:

Possible answer: Each country has reacted differently to independence. In Ukraine, movement toward economic progress has been slow. The country has had trouble establishing new trade links, and many Communist leaders, as well as the Soviet system of central planning, remain in place, making it difficult for the country to move toward a free-market economy. Agriculture, which is still organized in the inefficient state farms and collectives of the Soviet era, is a particular problem as Ukraine would like to increase productivity on its farmland. Belarus, meanwhile, is ruled by a reestablished Communist party. The country has a planned economy, and few people advocate a free-market economy.

In the Caucasus, Georgia is known for its people's business skills and enterprise, but its trading links are limited, and the country lacks sufficient energy resources. Armenia is developing its economy, but the country's conflict with Azerbaijan has hindered rapid economic progress. Azerbaijan is prosperous with large oil reserves that should provide income for many years. One result of independence for Azerbaijan is that now the country can export its oil around the world, not just to Russia.

Objective: 21

24. Answer:

Answers will vary. Many students will probably predict that Ukraine, with its rich agricultural potential, extensive mineral resources, and already developed industries, will be the most prosperous country in the region. Belarus, on the other hand, is resource-poor and does not seem likely to move toward a free-market economy in the near future. The nations of the Caucasus are held back from economic progress by internal ethnic conflicts and by conflicts with each other. Azerbaijan's extensive oil deposits could help the country prosper, but most of the Azerbaijan people remain farmers and herders.

Objective: 32

25. Answer:

Answers will vary. Some students may say that Ukraine should continue to claim Crimea as part of its territory, as the Crimean peninsula is physically connected to Ukraine and is a rich agricultural and mining region benefiting the country. Others may argue that Crimea, of which 70 percent of the population is ethnic Russian, should be part of Russia. Some students may support Crimea becoming independent so that it would have the power to govern its affairs. Students should consider, however, that Crimea's small territory and limited resources might hinder its viability as an independent country.

Objective: 12

CHAPTER 31

TEST QUESTIONS

Matching

Match the term with its correct description. One term is not used.

a. caravan
b. Qaraghandy
c. clan
d. Aral'sk
e. Amu Darya
f. Baikonur Cosmodrome

1. The center of Kazakhstan's major industrial region

2. One of the rivers that drains the Pamirs, carrying water to the deserts near the Aral Sea

3. A group of people descended from a common ancestral family

4. A former fishing port on the Aral Sea

5. The former Soviet Union's space port, located in Kazakhstan

Match the term with its correct description. One term is not used.

g. dryland agriculture
h. Tian Shan
i. oasis
j. state farm
k. Kara Kum
l. mosque

6. One of the world's largest and longest canals

7. A place in the desert where water can be found in springs, wells, or under dry riverbeds

8. A farming system that depends on rainfall rather than irrigation to water crops

9. An Islamic place of worship

10. A mountain range that passes through Kyrgystan and Uzbekistan

Multiple Choice

Circle the letter of the <u>best</u> answer.

11. Since achieving independence from the Soviet Union, the countries of Central Asia have
    a. adopted Communist governments.
    b. experienced economic decline.
    c. expanded their industrial bases.
    d. restored the water level of the Aral Sea.

12. The dominant faith in Central Asia is
   a. Eastern Orthodox Christianity.   b. Judaism.
   c. Roman Catholicism.   d. Islam.

13. Two Central Asian countries with large Russian populations are
   a. Kazakhstan and Krgyzstan.   b. Turkmenistan and Tajikistan.
   c. Uzbekistan and Tajikistan.   d. Krgyzstan and Turkmenistan.

14. Climates found in Central Asia include steppe, desert, and
   a. subarctic.   b. tropical.
   c. highland.   d. Mediterranean.

15. A resource that is particularly scarce in Central Asia and must be managed carefully is
   a. oil.   b. minerals.   c. water.   d. livestock.

16. Economic growth in Central Asia will depend on
   a. increased exports of minerals and cash crops.
   b. the formation of new state farms.
   c. the closing of Soviet-operated industries.
   d. slowing down a major population decline.

17. Many of Central Asia's southern cities began as
   a. trading centers along the Silk Road between Southwest Asia and China.
   b. farming collectives begun by the Soviet Union.
   c. fishing ports on the Aral Sea.
   d. farming villages in high mountain areas.

18. The Central Asian country that was most disrupted by the Soviet Union's 10-year occupation of Afghanistan is
   a. Kazakhstan.   b. Uzbekistan.
   c. Kyrgyzstan.   d. Tajikistan.

19. Except for the Tajiks, most of Central Asia's major groups speak
   a. Iranian.   b. Turkic languages.
   c. Germanic languages.   d. Polish.

20. A serious issue in Central Asia today is
   a. low birthrates.   b. immigration from Russia.
   c. high illiteracy rates.   d. increased military spending.

Short Answer

Answer the questions in the space provided.

21. What is dryland agriculture? Why did it not succeed in Central Asia during the Soviet era?
   _____
   _____
   _____
   _____
   _____

22. What landforms are found in Central Asia?
   _____
   _____
   _____
   _____
   _____

Critical Thinking

Write your answers on a separate sheet of paper.

23. How have the countries of Central Asia reacted to independence and the Soviet Union's collapse?

24. Could the damage suffered by the Aral Sea have been avoided? If so, how?

25. Many countries have provided foreign aid to the nations of Central Asia. Why do you think they are concerned with the economic progress of these somewhat isolated countries?

CHAPTER 31

TEST ANSWERS

Matching

1. Answer: b Objective: 32

2. Answer: e Objective: 12

3. Answer: c Objective: 32

4. Answer: d Objective: 12

5. Answer: f Objective: 31

6. Answer: k Objective: 12

7. Answer: i Objective: 12

8. Answer: g Objective: 32

9. Answer: l Objective: 21

10. Answer: h Objective: 11

Multiple Choice

11. Answer: b Objective: 22

12. Answer: d Objective: 21

13. Answer: a Objective: 32

14. Answer: c Objective: 11

15. Answer: c Objective: 12

16. Answer: a Objective: 22

17. Answer: a Objective: 21

18. Answer: d Objective: 31

19. Answer: b Objective: 21

20. Answer: c Objective: 22

Short Answer

21. Answer:
Dryland agriculture depends on rainfall rather than irrigation to water crops. It did not succeed in Central Asia during the Soviet era because of frequent droughts and dust storms.
Objective: 12

22. Answer:

Plains and low plateaus are the dominant landform in most of the region. Mountain ranges, such as the Kopet Mountains, the Pamirs, and the Tian Shan, are found in the south and east.

Objective: 11

Critical Thinking

23. Answer:

The countries of Central Asia have reacted differently to independence and the Soviet Union's collapse, though all have experienced economic decline. Kazakhstan, the second largest territory of the former Soviet Union, is privatizing collectives and state farms and selling the government's assets. Kyrgystan has worked to develop its mineral resources and to restore traditional land management. Uzbekistan and Turkmenistan, however, have changed little since independence and have retained strict central governments. The economies of these countries depend on industrialization and the development of natural resources. Finally, Tajikistan has experienced great turmoil since the collapse of the Soviet Union. Industry has nearly stopped, and conflicts between traditional and modern Tajiks have escalated.

Objective: 31

24. Answer:

Answers will vary. Some students may say that the Soviets were too aggressive in developing water resources in the area and did not consider the long-term consequences of their efforts. More efficient irrigation methods, focused on conserving water, might have prevented the shrinking of the Aral Sea, and crops might have been rotated, conserving the soil. Cotton, a crop that uses large amounts of water, might have been replaced with a different crop.

Objective: 12

25. Answer:

Possible answer: The countries of Central Asia lie in a strategic location, bordering China, Russia, and Southwest Asia. Contributing to the economic well-being of the Central Asian countries may lead to more influence in the region and thus greater control of Eurasian affairs in general. Additionally, many countries in the region have resources that, if developed, would benefit investors.

Objective: 22

UNIT 6

TEST QUESTIONS

Matching

Match the term with its correct description. One term is not used.

a. taiga
b. Commonwealth of Independent States
c. autarky
d. Bolsheviks
e. Mongols
f. Congress of People's Deputies

1. A policy under which a country strives for economic self-sufficiency

2. A warring people who invaded the Russian steppe in the thirteenth century

3. An association of former Soviet republics that serves as a forum for the discussion of shared problems

4. A huge forest of tall evergreen trees

5. The legislature of the new Russian government

Match the term with its correct description. One term is not used.

g. Mikhail Gorbachev
h. smelter
i. Boris Yeltsin
j. mosque
k. V. I. Lenin
l. soviet

6. The Bolshevik leader who became the Soviet Union's first leader

7. A factory that processes mineral ores

8. An Islamic place of worship

9. The Soviet Union's last leader, whose actions led to the country's breakup

10. The governing council of each republic in the USSR

Multiple Choice

Circle the letter of the <u>best</u> answer.

11. The least developed region of the former Soviet Union is
    a. Central Asia.
    b. the Caucasus.
    c. Russia's Volga region.
    d. Ukraine and Belarus.

12. Most of the people in Russia and northern Eurasia experience
    a. rainy winters and long, cool summers.
    b. warm, humid conditions all year long.
    c. long, cold winters and short summers.
    d. temperate weather for farming all year long.

13. The Ural Mountains form much of the boundary between
    a. Russia and China.
    b. Europe and Asia.
    c. Southwest Asia and Central Asia.
    d. The Black Sea and the Caspian Sea.

14. Two countries that have kept a strong central government and central economic planning since independence from the Soviet Union are
    a. Russia and Azerbaijan.   b. St. Petersburg and Siberia.
    c. Belarus and Uzbekistan.   d. Armenia and Kazakhstan.

15. All of the following physical features are found in Russia and Northern Eurasia except
    a. tropical rain forests.   b. deserts.
    c. high mountains.   d. grassy plains.

16. The largest ethnic group in the Russian Federation is made up of
    a. Russians.   b. Ukrainians.   c. Armenians.   d. Kazakhs.

17. The series of events that led to the Communist Revolution began with droughts and food shortages in the 1890s and ended with
    a. World War II.
    b. riots in several large cities in 1905 and 1906.
    c. the failure of a short-lived republic set up after the czar's abdication in 1917.
    d. Stalin coming to power in 1924.

18. Since ancient times the economic prosperity of Ukraine has been most closely tied to the country's abundance of
    a. the taiga.   b. fertile soil.
    c. oil.   d. natural gas.

19. Since the breakup of the Soviet Union, economic reforms have
    a. made most people feel secure.
    b. soothed conflicts among competitive regions.
    c. relieved the problems of unemployment and crime.
    d. led to the diversification of industry.

20. A policy of open discussion, called *glasnost,* of Soviet problems began under the leadership of
    a. Catherine the Great.   b. Karl Marx.
    c. Boris Yeltsin.   d. Mikhail Gorbachev.

Short Answer

Answer the questions in the space provided.

21. What was the Cold War, and when did it take place?
    _____
    _____
    _____
    _____
    _____

22. Why was a shortage of consumer goods a problem in the Soviet Union?

_____
_____
_____
_____
_____
_____

Critical Thinking

Write your answers on a separate sheet of paper.

23. Describe the events that led to the creation of the Soviet Union and its command economy.

24. The former Soviet republics are now independent countries. Some of them, such as Georgia and Tajikistan, are experiencing violent and disruptive ethnic conflicts. Do you think the other members of the Commonwealth of Independent States should intervene to help resolve these disputes? Why or why not?

25. Was the breakup of the Soviet Union inevitable? Give reasons to support your answer.

UNIT 6

TEST ANSWERS

Matching

1.Answer: c Objective: 62

2.Answer: e Objective: 61

3.Answer: b Objective: 63

4.Answer: a Objective: 65

5.Answer: f Objective: 63

6.Answer: k Objective: 61

7.Answer: h Objective: 64

8.Answer: j Objective: 63

9.Answer: g Objective: 62

10.Answer: l Objective: 62

Multiple Choice

11.Answer: a Objective: 64

12.Answer: c Objective: 65

13.Answer: b Objective: 65

14.Answer: c Objective: 63

15.Answer: a Objective: 65

16.Answer: a Objective: 63

17.Answer: c Objective: 61

18.Answer: b Objective: 64

19.Answer: d Objective: 67

20.Answer: d Objective: 62

Short Answer

21.Answer:
The Cold War was a political struggle between the United States and the Soviet Union that continued for more than 40 years after the end of World War II. The two superpowers competed in arms production and space exploration, and vied for the support of other countries.

Objective: 62

22. Answer:
   The Soviet government made heavy industry and the production of military goods a priority. As a result, consumer goods were not produced in large quantities.

   Objective: 62

Critical Thinking

23. Answer:
   Possible answer: In the late nineteenth century, Russia was primarily a country of poor farmers, whose economic condition was Russia's greatest problem. In the 1890s, droughts, food shortages, and a global economic depression that slowed trade and reduced exports made life harder for many Russians. These conditions led to riots in several large cities in 1905 and 1906. New economic programs were begun, but they did not bring about major changes.
   Thus by the start of World War I in 1914, Russia was in a shaky position. The war then took a heavy toll on the country. Because of the hardships brought on by war and the numerous internal problems, the czar abdicated in 1917. Although a temporary republic was established, it was soon overthrown by the Bolshevik Party. The Bolsheviks wanted to mold Russia according to the ideas of Karl Marx, who believed that workers were victims of capitalism, and V. I. Lenin proposed government ownership of farms and factories as the solution. Once the Union of Soviet Socialist Republics was established, all economic and political decisions were made by the Communist government in Moscow.

   Objective: 61

24. Answer:
   Answers will vary. Students supporting intervention will probably argue that these conflicts, by weakening the countries' economies, have had a damaging effect on the economy of the region as a whole and thus it would be in the best interests of the region for members of the Commonwealth to intervene. Other students may argue that these former republics must be allowed to conduct their own affairs, and that intervention might even increase regional conflict.

   Objective: 63

25. Answer:
   Answers will vary. Some students may point out that the Soviet economic system was inefficient in many ways, and product quality was low. People were tired of sacrifices without gains and were ready for a change. Mikhail Gorbachev raised people's hope for change, and his reforms of *glasnost* and *perestroika* weakened the Soviet central government. Even without these reforms, however, it is likely that the Soviet economy would have continued to grow weaker as much of the developed world moved away from heavy industries toward consumer goods and service industries, and that the government would have experienced more pressure from its discontented citizens and ethnic groups. Some students may suggest that if Soviet leaders had been more attuned to the frustrations of the people and had taken greater steps earlier to ease these frustrations, the Soviet Union might have survived.

   Objective: 62

CHAPTER 32

TEST QUESTIONS

Matching

Match the term with its correct description. One term is not used.

a. Qur'an
b. fossil water
c. Bedouin
d. exotic river
e. drip irrigation
f. Muslim

1. A person who follows Islam

2. A member of a Southwest Asian group that migrates from one desert area to another

3. The sacred book of Islam

4. A stream that flows from a humid environment across a desert into a sea

5. Water that is not replaced by rainfall

Match the term with its correct description. One term is not used.

g. Judaism
h. Islam
i. monotheism
j. fundamentalism
k. secularism
l. Christianity

6. The first major religion to center around the belief in a single god

7. The belief in one god

8. The religion founded by the prophet Muhammad

9. An indifference to or rejection of religion

10. The religion that eventually became the main faith of the Roman Empire

Multiple Choice

Circle the letter of the <u>best</u> answer.

11. The politics of Southwest Asia are dominated by the
    a. concern about diminishing oil resources.
    b. Arab-Israeli conflict.
    c. conflicting needs of Bedouins and city dwellers.
    d. conflict between the Kurds and Zoroastrians.

12. The Mesopotamian people who developed writing were the
    a. Assyrians.
    b. Phoenicians.
    c. Ottomans.
    d. Sumerians.

13. Important issues in Southwest Asia include all of the following except
    a. the dominance of Christians over other groups in the region.
    b. the political power of oil-rich nations.
    c. conflicts over water resources.
    d. rising populations.

14. In many parts of Southwest Asia, irrigation water is provided by
    a. deep wells.
    b. large freshwater lakes.
    c. imports of water from other world regions.
    d. abundant rainfall.

15. A major occupation in much of Southwest Asia is
    a. coal mining.
    b. fishing.
    c. manufacturing.
    d. agriculture.

16. The followers of the religion of ancient Persia are called the
    a. Kurds.
    b. Israelis.
    c. Zoroastrians.
    d. Bedouins.

17. All of the following resources are scarce in Southwest Asia except
    a. fresh water.
    b. coal.
    c. oil.
    d. forests.

18. Rivers can exist in the desert regions of Southwest Asia because
    a. they usually are located near oases.
    b. irrigation maintains the water that they supply.
    c. groundwater provides the extra water they need to flow.
    d. they usually start in the more humid mountain regions.

19. Of the following historical events, the event that took place most recently was
    a. the agreement between Israel and the Palestinians providing for Palestinian self-rule in certain areas.
    b. the collapse of the Ottoman Empire.
    c. the birth of Muhammad and the spread of Islam across Southwest Asia.
    d. the Southwest Asian countries' achievement of independence from European colonial rule.

20. The only country in the region where commercial agriculture is widespread is
    a. Iran.   b. Turkey.   c. Israel.   d. Jordan.

Short Answer

Answer the questions in the space provided.

21. List the climates found in Southwest Asia.

    _____
    _____
    _____
    _____
    _____

22. Why has conflict existed between the Arabs and the Israelis?

    _____
    _____
    _____
    _____
    _____

224

Critical Thinking

Write your answers on a separate sheet of paper.

23. Briefly describe the major religions that originated in Southwest Asia.

24. The area between the Tigris and Euphrates rivers is sometimes called the "cradle of civilization." Why do you think this is?

25. How might the price of oil on the world market be affected as Southwest Asia undergoes greater development? Explain.

CHAPTER 32

TEST ANSWERS

Matching

1. Answer: f Objective: 22

2. Answer: c Objective: 22

3. Answer: a Objective: 22

4. Answer: d Objective: 11

5. Answer: b Objective: 12

6. Answer: g Objective: 22

7. Answer: i Objective: 22

8. Answer: h Objective: 22

9. Answer: k Objective: 22

10. Answer: l Objective: 22

Multiple Choice

11. Answer: b Objective: 23

12. Answer: d Objective: 21

13. Answer: a Objective: 23

14. Answer: a Objective: 12

15. Answer: d Objective: 12

16. Answer: c Objective: 22

17. Answer: c Objective: 12

18. Answer: d Objective: 11

19. Answer: a Objective: 21

20. Answer: c Objective: 12

Short Answer

21. Answer:
    Most of Southwest Asia has a desert climate. Steppe climates are found on high interior plateaus and along the edges of the deserts. A Mediterranean climate is found in coastal areas next to the Mediterranean Sea.

    Objective: 11

22. Answer:

The Jewish people of Israel view themselves as descendants of the ancient Hebrews, who lived in Southwest Asia about 3,000 years ago. By the seventh century, however, few Jews remained in the region, and Arabs made up most of the population. The Jewish state of Israel, created in 1948, is located in the midst of the Arab countries and is bitterly opposed by some Arabs. Both groups see the area as their homeland.

Objective: 23

Critical Thinking

23. Answer:

The major religions of Judaism, Christianity, and Islam all originated in Southwest Asia. Judaism, the religion of the Jews, appeared between 3500 B.C. and 600 B.C. in Palestine, the site of present-day Israel. Judaism was the first major monotheistic religion—a religion that worships one god.

Christianity, founded on the teachings of Jesus Christ, developed from Judaism and spread during the Roman era. It eventually became the major religion of the Roman Empire. Later, it split into the Eastern Orthodox and the Roman Catholic churches.

Islam, the most widespread religion of Southwest Asia today, was founded by the prophet Muhammad, who, Muslims believe, received the word of God, which was then recorded in the Qur'an, the Muslims' sacred book. Today, Islam is a unifying culture trait of Southwest Asia.

Objective: 22

24. Answer:

This area, also called the Fertile Crescent, contains wide plains of productive land. These plains supported the world's first civilizations and a variety of innovations. Hence the region can be considered the birthplace, or cradle, of civilization and of many of the ways of life that have remained important over the centuries, such as writing and the domestication of plants and animals.

Objective: 21

25. Answer:

Possible answer: As the countries of Southwest Asia become more developed, their own need for oil will increase. Consequently, the region will be able to export less oil, and the price of oil will rise. Also, many of the countries have supported the financial costs of development with profits from oil exports. If development becomes increasingly expensive, the countries may try to raise the price of oil to compensate for the rise in costs.

Objective: 23

CHAPTER 33

TEST QUESTIONS

Matching

Match the term with its correct description. One term is not used.

a. kibbutz
b. Ankara
c. minaret
d. Amman
e. Taurus
f. Holocaust

1. The persecution and killing of millions of Jews by Nazi Germany during World War II

2. A mountain range in southern Turkey

3. The tower of a mosque

4. An Israeli collective farm

5. The capital city of Turkey

Match the term with its correct description. One term is not used.

g. Damascus
h. Cyprus
i. Tel Aviv
j. Judaism
k. Zionism
l. Negev

6. The largest city in Israel

7. An island that is a site of conflict between Greeks and Turks

8. A movement that began in the nineteenth century to establish a Jewish state in Palestine

9. A rocky desert in Israel, southwest of the Dead Sea

10. Syria's capital city and an ancient center of Islamic civilization

Multiple Choice

Circle the letter of the best answer.

11. Turkey's two main climate types are
    a. humid tropical and tropical savanna.
    b. humid continental and humid tropical.
    c. marine west coast and desert.
    d. Mediterranean and steppe.

12. The least developed part of Turkey is the
   a. eastern mountains.
   b. coastline of the Aegean Sea.
   c. Balkan Peninsula.
   d. area surrounding Istanbul.

13. The people in Jordan who outnumber the country's original inhabitants are the
   a. Jews.
   b. Christians.
   c. Palestinians.
   d. Lebanese.

14. The country that has led the Arab opposition to Israel is
   a. Cyprus.   b. Syria.   c. Turkey.   d. Lebanon.

15. 'Aqaba is
   a. the strait that separates European Turkey from Asian Turkey.
   b. the cultural center of Israel.
   c. an important port city in Jordan.
   d. a river that provides most of Syria's irrigation water.

16. The economy of Lebanon is unstable because the country
   a. is one of the least developed countries in the Eastern Mediterranean region.
   b. is located far from the trade routes of the Mediterranean Sea.
   c. has been a target of foreign investment.
   d. has been wracked by periodic civil wars and the Arab-Israeli conflict.

17. Syria stretches from the mountainous Mediterranean coast to the
   a. Pontic Mountains.
   b. plains of Mesopotamia.
   c. Dead Sea.
   d. Negev Desert.

18. Istanbul is Turkey's leading seaport because it
   a. is located in Turkey's most underdeveloped region.
   b. is the starting point of an oil pipeline running to the Mediterranean Sea.
   c. became the capital of the modern Turkish republic in 1923.
   d. is located on the straits connecting the Black and Mediterranean seas.

19. Before Israel became a nation,
   a. Great Britain granted independence to Palestine.
   b. the Sinai Peninsula was returned to Egypt.
   c. Palestinians were granted self-rule in Gaza and the West Bank.
   d. the Six-Day War broke out.

20. Agricultural progress in Syria depends on
   a. the development of more water resources.
   b. the reduced use of fertilizers.
   c. the processing of food products for export.
   d. the country's ability to control a growing insect problem.

Short Answer

Answer the questions in the space provided.

21. What is Israel's National Water Carrier project?

_____
_____
_____
_____
_____

22. Why was Turkey's capital moved in 1923?

_____

_____

_____

_____

_____

Critical Thinking

Write your answers on a separate sheet of paper.

23. How has Israel been able to become a developed nation?

24. How might Lebanon recover from the problems that have plagued it over the past few decades? Do you think other nations should offer assistance? Explain.

25. To whom do you think present-day Israel should belong—Israelis, Palestinians, or both? Explain.

CHAPTER 33

TEST ANSWERS

Matching

    1.Answer: f Objective: 22

    2.Answer: e Objective: 11

    3.Answer: c Objective: 31

    4.Answer: a Objective: 21

    5.Answer: b Objective: 11

    6.Answer: i Objective: 21

    7.Answer: h Objective: 12

    8.Answer: k Objective: 22

    9.Answer: l Objective: 21

    10.Answer: g Objective: 31

Multiple Choice

    11.Answer: d Objective: 11

    12.Answer: a Objective: 11

    13.Answer: c Objective: 32

    14.Answer: b Objective: 32

    15.Answer: c Objective: 31

    16.Answer: d Objective: 32

    17.Answer: b Objective: 31

    18.Answer: d Objective: 11

    19.Answer: a Objective: 22

    20.Answer: a Objective: 31

Short Answer

21.Answer:
The National Water Carrier is a sophisticated and highly efficient water management system. Its pipelines carry water from the Sea of Galilee through central Israel to the northern borders of the Negev Desert. It allows irrigation agriculture, even in dry areas.

Objective: 21

22. Answer:
    When the Turkish republic was formed in 1923, the capital was moved from Istanbul in the far western part of the country to more centrally located Ankara. Ankara is the center of railroad transportation for the whole country and is assisting in the development of eastern Turkey.

    Objective: 12

Critical Thinking

23. Answer:
    Possible response: With few resources and relatively little fertile land, Israel has relied on its most valuable resource—its skilled people. In addition, sophisticated farming methods and major water projects have enabled commercial agriculture to thrive in Israel. Israel has also developed high-tech industries that manufacture products such as computers, military weapons, and precision engineering equipment. Another factor that contributes to Israel's prosperity is its appeal as a tourist attraction. People come from all over the world to visit Israel's holy places and its sunny beaches. Israel also receives a considerable amount of foreign aid from Jews around the world and from the United States.

    Objective: 21

24. Answer:
    Answers will vary. Some students might say that Christian and Muslim forces within Lebanon, which have been the main opponents in a multitude of civil wars in the country since the 1950s, must come to a peaceful accord. Some might argue that the United Nations should maintain a presence in the region until Lebanon can create a stable government and rebuild its economy. In the meantime, as other students may point out, a reduction in tension between Arabs and Israelis may benefit Lebanon. Furthermore, if a Palestinian homeland were formed, the hundreds of thousands of Palestinian refugees now in Lebanon might be able to leave. This, too, would reduce conflict in the country, some of which has been caused by or worsened because of the refugee issue.

    Objective: 32

25. Answer:
    Answers will vary. Some students may say that the Israelis, who did not have a homeland before the creation of the Israeli state in 1948, should continue to make the region their homeland. Others may say that the Palestinians were displaced when the Jewish state was formed and that present-day Israel should become a Palestinian state. Still others may express hope that Israelis and Palestinians could share the land and resources and live together in peace.

    Objective: 22

CHAPTER 34

TEST QUESTIONS

Matching

Match the term with its correct description. One term is not used.

a. Tehran
b. theocracy
c. sultanate
d. Sanaa
e. Baghdad
f. pilgrimage

1. Iran's capital and most industrialized city

2. A country governed by religious law

3. A journey, often for religious purposes, such as that taken by Muslims to Mecca

4. A country that is ruled by a Muslim monarch

5. Iraq's capital city, located on the banks of the Tigris River

Match the term with its correct description. One term is not used.

g. arable
h. Shi`a
i. Pathan
j. fallow
k. perimeter
l. qanat

6. Unused, such as Iraqi croplands every two or three years

7. A branch of Islam that is the dominant religion in Iran

8. A long tunnel that carries water from springs at the foot of the mountains to the plains of Iran

9. An outer boundary, as of the Arabian Peninsula

10. The largest ethnic group in Afghanistan

Multiple Choice

Circle the letter of the <u>best</u> answer.

11. The areas of densest settlement in Iraq are located
    a. in the western deserts and dry grasslands.
    b. on the plains along rivers and irrigation canals.
    c. in the northern mountain valleys.
    d. in the country's marine-west-coast climate region.

12. The oil industry has provided Saudi Arabia with all of the following except
    a. a large number of jobs for the country's people.
    b. the money to build factories and modern farms.
    c. political power in the region and in the world.
    d. government-paid social services.

13. Historically, many peoples have been attracted to Afghanistan because of its
    a. rich oil deposits.   b. fertile soils and good rainfall.
    c. stable government.   d. strategic location.

14. The country in Interior Southwest Asia that formed in 1990 when two separate countries merged is
    a. Yemen.   b. Iraq.
    c. Saudi Arabia.   d. Oman.

15. A major challenge to farmers in Iraq is
    a. the buildup of salts in the soil.
    b. heavy rains that cause floods and ruin crops.
    c. outdated pipelines that leak oil onto farmlands.
    d. the high percentage of land that is arable.

16. A large uninhabited area in the southeastern corner of Saudi Arabia is called the
    a. Hindu Kush.   b. Khyber Pass.
    c. Rub' al-Khali.   d. Arabian Peninsula.

17. Iraq and Iran both import large quantities of
    a. oil.   b. food.   c. water.   d. wool.

18. An important event that took place in Interior Southwest Asia in 1990 was the
    a. start of a long war between Iran and Iraq.
    b. election of the Shah as Iran's ruler.
    c. invasion of Kuwait by Iraq.
    d. construction of Saudi Arabia's first desalinization plant.

19. Goods produced in Iran that are important to the country's economy include
    a. computers and corn.   b. weapons and fish.
    c. nuts and rugs.   d. books and gold.

20. After the Shah fled Iran in 1979,
    a. a fundamentalist Islamic government came to power.
    b. feuds between ethnic Persians and other ethnic groups stopped.
    c. Iran nationalized its oil industry.
    d. the Soviet Union began a 10-year occupation of the country.

Short Answer

Answer the questions in the space provided.

21. What are the countries of the Arabian perimeter?

    _____
    _____
    _____
    _____
    _____

22. Where do most of the people of Saudi Arabia live?

    _____
    _____
    _____
    _____
    _____

Critical Thinking

Write your answers on a separate sheet of paper.

23. What might Iran, Iraq, and the countries of the Arabian Peninsula be like today if oil had not been discovered in these countries? Give specific examples to support your answer.

24. Several countries of Interior Southwest Asia have rejected Westernization, while others have embraced it. Do you think countries should always attempt to preserve their traditional values and customs? Provide examples to support your point of view.

25. How might a war among the countries of Interior Southwest Asia affect the price of oil on the world market?

CHAPTER 34

TEST ANSWERS

Matching

1. Answer: a Objective: 21

2. Answer: b Objective: 22

3. Answer: f Objective: 31

4. Answer: c Objective: 42

5. Answer: e Objective: 11

6. Answer: j Objective: 12

7. Answer: h Objective: 22

8. Answer: l Objective: 21

9. Answer: k Objective: 41

10. Answer: i Objective: 23

Multiple Choice

11. Answer: b Objective: 11

12. Answer: a Objective: 32

13. Answer: d Objective: 23

14. Answer: a Objective: 42

15. Answer: a Objective: 12

16. Answer: c Objective: 31

17. Answer: b Objective: 21

18. Answer: c Objective: 12

19. Answer: c Objective: 21

20. Answer: a Objective: 22

Short Answer

21. Answer:
    The countries of the Arabian perimeter are Kuwait, the United Arab Emirates, Qatar, Bahrain, Oman, and Yemen.

    Objective: 41

22. Answer:

Most of the people of Saudi Arabia live where there is either water or oil. Mecca in the western mountains and Riyadh in the country's interior were built around oases. The oil fields along the Persian Gulf were settled more recently.

Objective: 31

Critical Thinking

23. Answer:

Possible answer: Oil revenue has made possible the political, military, and economic development of most of Interior Southwest Asia. The greatest difference would probably be in the cities and in most of the Arabian Peninsula states, where people's lives have changed dramatically since the discovery of oil. Without oil, for example, Saudi Arabia would have little money to industrialize or to provide government services to its people.

On the other hand, without the discovery of oil, there might be less contact and less conflict between traditional and Western values, and the internal affairs of these nations might not have as great an effect on global issues.

As for the lives of people in the region who depend on herding and traditional agriculture, their ways of life might be much the same now as before the discovery of oil. Without the discovery of oil, however, more people might be engaged in these traditional ways of life, as increased development and opportunities brought about by the discovery of oil probably attracted rural dwellers to the cities. In addition, urbanization and development resulting from the discovery of oil might have interfered with migration patterns.

Objective: 12

24. Answer:

Answers will vary. Students might consider the ramification of Westernization in countries such as Iraq, Iran, or other countries with which they may be familiar. Some students may say that it is possible to preserve some traditional customs despite the adoption of new ones. Students should provide specific examples to support their points of view.

Objective: 22

25. Answer:

Possible answer: A war in the region might disrupt the production of oil, thus reducing the world oil supply and thereby raising prices. Some countries might refuse to ship oil to enemy supporters, again limiting the supply and raising the price of oil.

Objective: 32

UNIT 7

TEST QUESTIONS

Matching

Match the term with its correct description. One term is not used.

a. Kuwait
b. Jerusalem
c. Islam
d. Bedouin
e. Christianity
f. Zionism

1. The movement to establish a Jewish state in Palestine

2. An oil-rich nation of the Arabian perimeter

3. The religion founded by Muhammad

4. A migrating herder who roams the outer parts of the Southwest Asian deserts

5. A holy city for Jews, Muslims, and Christians

Match the term with its correct description. One term is not used.

g. qanat
h. Rub' al-Khali
i. Istanbul
j. kibbutz
k. Negev Desert
l. Mecca

6. Islam's most important city, located in Saudi Arabia

7. An Israeli collective farm

8. A large, uninhabited region on the Arabian Peninsula

9. A Turkish city located on the straits between Europe and Asia

10. A long tunnel that carries water from springs at the foot of the mountains to the plains of Iran

Multiple Choice

Circle the letter of the <u>best</u> answer.

11. The sacred book of Islam is called the
    a. Qu'ran.   b. Bible.
    c. Rub' al-Khali.   d. Sunni.

12. Agriculture in Southwest Asia depends mainly on
    a. foreign aid.
    b. modern farming techniques.
    c. Bedouin migrations.
    d. irrigation and water availability.

13. Large numbers of people in all of the following culture groups live in Southwest Asia except
    a. Jews.   b. Muslims.   c. Kurds.   d. Georgians.

14. Oman, Yemen, and the United Arab Emirates belong to the Arabian perimeter, which is a(n)
    a. group formed to control the price of oil on the world market.
    b. organization of Muslim countries in Southwest Asia.
    c. group of countries surrounding Saudi Arabia on the Arabian Peninsula.
    d. region in western Iraq through which several exotic rivers flow.

15. Of the following countries, the one that has experienced the least internal or regional conflict in recent decades is
    a. Oman.   b. Israel.   c. Iran.   d. Lebanon.

16. The most economically developed county of Southwest Asia is
    a. Afghanistan.   b. Israel.
    c. Iraq.   d. Yemen.

17. While the oil industry provides many Southwest Asian nations with much income, it provides few jobs because
    a. the industry is highly mechanized.
    b. there are not enough skilled workers.
    c. little oil is pumped when prices are low.
    d. foreign companies control all oil refining facilities.

18. Little arable land is found in Afghanistan because
    a. much farmland has been lost to environmental damage.
    b. most of the country is dry and mountainous.
    c. the country is landlocked.
    d. most farmland is limited to commercial plantations.

19. The climate type that dominates Southwest Asia is
    a. desert.   b. highland.
    c. humid continental.   d. steppe.

20. The dominant religions in Israel and Iran are, respectively,
    a. Islam and Christianity.
    b. Christianity and Judaism.
    c. Zoroastrianism and Zionism.
    d. Judaism and Islam.

Short Answer

Answer the questions in the space provided.

21. Where are major cities and farmland generally found in Southwest Asia?
    _____
    _____
    _____
    _____
    _____

22. When and how did Israel become a nation?

_____
_____
_____
_____
_____
_____

Critical Thinking

Write your answers on a separate sheet of paper.

23. Explain the significance of Southwest Asia's location.

24. Three of the world's major religions originated in the relatively small region of Southwest Asia. Why do you think this is so?

25. If you looked at an economic resource map of Southwest Asia, you would see that farming areas are located in isolated spots in Saudi Arabia, while in most other areas in the region, farming activity occurs in long, wide, continuous bands. Explain this pattern of farming activity in the region.

UNIT 7

TEST ANSWERS

Matching

1. Answer: f Objective: 73

2. Answer: a Objective: 71

3. Answer: c Objective: 73

4. Answer: d Objective: 72

5. Answer: b Objective: 73

6. Answer: l Objective: 73

7. Answer: j Objective: 71

8. Answer: h Objective: 72

9. Answer: i Objective: 75

10. Answer: g Objective: 71

Multiple Choice

11. Answer: a Objective: 73

12. Answer: d Objective: 71

13. Answer: d Objective: 74

14. Answer: c Objective: 75

15. Answer: a Objective: 74

16. Answer: b Objective: 71

17. Answer: a Objective: 74

18. Answer: b Objective: 72

19. Answer: a Objective: 71

20. Answer: d Objective: 73

Short Answer

21. Answer:
Major cities and farmland are generally located in river valleys, along coastlines, and on other sites where water is available. Some cities have also grown near oil deposits.

Objective: 72

22. Answer:
    After the Holocaust in World War II, many nations were sympathetic to the Jews, who had suffered much persecution not only during the war but also over several centuries in different world regions. Calls for a Jewish homeland, or a place where Jews might live free from persecution and outside control, received greater attention after the war. As a result, in 1948 the United Nations established the state of Israel in Palestine, a region in Southwest Asia, as a homeland for Jews. Great Britain had recently given the region its independence.

    Objective: 74

Critical Thinking

23. Answer:
    Possible answer: Southwest Asia is a crossroads connecting Europe, Africa, and Central and eastern Asia. Because it is a crossroads, wars, ethnic conflicts, and economic downturns in the region affect affairs on all three continents. For example, a war in Southwest Asia could disrupt international trade on the region's rivers, straits, and gulfs.

    Objective: 75

24. Answer:
    Possible answer: The fertile plains of Mesopotamia and other fertile areas in Southwest Asia supported the growth of early civilizations that developed these three major religions—Islam, Judaism, and Christianity. Southwest Asia's strategic trade location between Europe, Africa, and Central and eastern Asia then helped these civilizations and their religions thrive and spread around the world.

    Objective: 73

25. Answer:
    Possible answer: In Saudi Arabia, most farming relies on the water of oases instead of that of rivers. Oases are not connected and thus farming areas in Saudi Arabia appear on a economic resource map as isolated dots in the desert. In many other areas of Southwest Asia, however, farming relies on rivers such as the Euphrates and Tigris. As a result, farming activity on a resource map appears in these areas as continuous bands following these rivers.

    Objective: 76

CHAPTER 35

TEST QUESTIONS

Matching

Match the term with its correct description. One term is not used.

a. Sahel
b. animism
c. Niger
d. Namib
e. malaria
f. Orange

1. A sparsely vegetated coastal desert in Southern Africa

2. A traditional belief in nature and spiritual beings

3. A river that flows from Africa's western highlands northeast to an inland delta and then south to the Atlantic

4. A drought-prone region of bush savannas and grasslands along the southern edge of the Sahara

5. A river in Southern Africa

Match the term with its correct description. One term is not used.

g. El Djouf
h. Great Zimbabwe
i. rift
j. tsetse
k. Axum
l. escarpment

6. A steep slope capped by a nearly flat plateau

7. A powerful ancient civilization based in the highlands of Ethiopia

8. A basin along the southern edge of the Sahara that contains the inland delta of the Niger River

9. An ancient city in Southern Africa that began as a village of ironworkers

10. A deep valley that cuts through highlands, such as in eastern Africa

Multiple Choice

Circle the letter of the <u>best</u> answer.

11. Africa is rich in all of the following except
    a. mineral resources.   b. fertile land.
    c. cultural diversity.   d. a variety of climates.

12. Most of Africa's rivers
    a. have waterfalls or rapids near the coast.
    b. empty into the Indian Ocean.
    c. are located in West Africa.
    d. are very short and flow from east to west.

13. Europeans began to explore the interior of the African continent
    a. during the height of the Kush empire in western Africa.
    b. during the fourteenth and fifteenth centuries.
    c. when the first slave-trading posts were built.
    d. a few hundred years after the slave trade began.

14. African populations have increased during the past 25 years largely as a result of
    a. people moving to Africa to find work.
    b. the elimination of most diseases.
    c. the adoption of more modern health practices.
    d. improvements in housing for urban dwellers.

15. Ancient empires in western Africa grew powerful by
    a. controlling trade across the Sahara.
    b. conquering peoples in the Persian Gulf region.
    c. developing commercial farming techniques.
    d. building plantations in the Americas.

16. As one moves away from the rain forests of Africa,
    a. rains increase and tall grasses become dominant.
    b. the climate becomes drier and trees become shorter.
    c. elevations increase and temperatures become warmer.
    d. the Mediterranean climate becomes dominant.

17. Organizations like the Economic Community of West African States have been formed to
    a. develop the mineral resources of eastern and northern Africa.
    b. encourage the export of more goods to countries in the Northern Hemisphere.
    c. create cooperation between countries so that goods and workers can cross borders more
       freely.
    d. limit development to the production of goods that will meet the needs of local markets.

18. Since 1950, most African countries have
    a. become independent from European colonial rule.
    b. become self-sufficient in food production.
    c. fully developed their natural resources.
    d. redrawn their borders along ethnic group lines.

19. If you prefer weather that is mild and cool all year, you would probably choose to live
    a. in the Kalahari.   b. in the Zaire River basin.
    c. in the highlands of Kenya.   d. along the Mediterranean coast.

20. In the future, Africa may be a major source of the world's supply of
    a. coal.   b. hydroelectric power.
    c. nuclear power.   d. natural gas.

Short Answer

Answer the questions in the space provided.

21. How were the five major African basins formed?

    _____
    _____
    _____
    _____
    _____

248

22. Where is the Sahel located? Why is it expanding?

_____
_____
_____
_____
_____
_____

Critical Thinking

Write your answers on a separate sheet of paper.

23. How did European colonization contribute to Africa's current economic challenges?

24. Why do you think few people live in the tropical rain forests of Africa?

25. What steps do you think African countries should take to develop their economic resources?

CHAPTER 35

TEST ANSWERS

Matching

    1.Answer: d Objective: 12

    2.Answer: b Objective: 31

    3.Answer: c Objective: 11

    4.Answer: a Objective: 12

    5.Answer: f Objective: 11

    6.Answer: l Objective: 11

    7.Answer: k Objective: 21

    8.Answer: g Objective: 11

    9.Answer: h Objective: 21

   10.Answer: i Objective: 11

Multiple Choice

  11.Answer: b Objective: 32

  12.Answer: a Objective: 11

  13.Answer: d Objective: 22

  14.Answer: c Objective: 31

  15.Answer: a Objective: 21

  16.Answer: b Objective: 12

  17.Answer: c Objective: 32

  18.Answer: a Objective: 22

  19.Answer: c Objective: 12

  20.Answer: b Objective: 32

Short Answer

  21.Answer:
    Before the supercontinent Gondwanaland broke up, these basins—El Djouf, the Chad Basin, the Sudan Basin, the Zaire Basin, and the Kalahari Basin—were the ending points for major rivers. The rivers later cut channels to the sea, but the basins remained.
    Objective: 11

22. Answer:
   The Sahel is located along the southern edge of the Sahara. This region frequently experiences drought. The movement of people and cattle away from the drought-stricken regions has led to overgrazing and the expansion of the desert.

   Objective: 12

Critical Thinking

23. Answer:
   Possible answer: The political boundaries established by European powers in the nineteenth century did not take economic needs into account. The borders drawn by Europeans left some countries landlocked, without access to the ocean and world trade. Some countries fell under one climate region, limiting agricultural production to certain kinds of crops. Others were formed with small land area and small populations, providing few skilled workers and limited markets for goods. All of these factors have created economic challenges to the countries of Africa today.

   Objective: 22

24. Answer:
   Possible answer: Poor soil makes farming difficult. In addition, disease, such as sleeping sickness, which is carried by the tsetse fly, poses a threat both to humans and farm animals in humid-tropical regions. Limited accessibility may be another factor.

   Objective: 12

25. Answer:
   Possible answer: Providing increased education and training, particularly in technical fields, may be an important factor in Africa's future economic development. Cooperation among countries, trading goods within the continent instead of exporting them, and allowing workers to freely cross borders may also help.

   Objective: 32

CHAPTER 36

TEST QUESTIONS

Matching

Match the term with its correct description. One term is not used.

a. Carthage
b. erg
c. Nile River
d. Cairo
e. Suez Canal
f. reg

1. A large amount of sand covering a basin in the Sahara

2. A waterway that connects the Red Sea to the Mediterranean Sea

3. An ancient Tunisian city that once controlled Mediterranean trade

4. Egypt's capital city, located on the Nile River

5. A gravel-covered plain formed when wind blows dust and sand away from the land's surface

Match the term with its correct description. One term is not used.

g. capital
h. *sebka*
i. Aswan
j. Ahaggar
k. silt
l. free port

6. Fertile sediment deposited by the flooding Nile onto farm fields

7. Any source of wealth, such as money or machinery, used to produce more wealth

8. The Sahara's highland region, located in Algeria

9. The location of the Nile's largest dam, which provides one-third of Egypt's electricity

10. A place, such as Tangier, Morocco, where few or no taxes are placed on goods unloaded there

Multiple Choice

Circle the letter of the best answer.

11. Of all Arab countries, Algeria has the
    a. lowest rate of population growth.
    b. highest proportion of factory workers.
    c. poorest infrastructure.
    d. greatest self-sufficiency in food.

12. The Sahara is dry because it
    a. is far from the Nile River and the Mediterranean Sea.
    b. has been overgrazed and overpopulated.
    c. is far from the ocean and blocked by mountains.
    d. has few plants to prevent erosion.

13. Considerable tension exists in Egypt between
    a. Arab regionalists and Egyption nationalists.
    b. Islamic fundamentalists and Arab regionalists.
    c. European colonists and native Africans.
    d. Cairo residents and Alexandria residents.

14. The North African country that has coastlines on both the Mediterranean Sea and the Atlantic Ocean is
    a. Libya.   b. Egypt.   c. Algeria.   d. Morocco.

15. In Egypt, the advantage of perennial irrigation over basin irrigation is that
    a. fertile sediment is deposited on the land in annual floods.
    b. the use of fertilizers is not necessary.
    c. two or three crops can be grown instead of only one.
    d. disease-causing organisms cannot survive.

16. Ancient Egyptians believed that the Nile was a gift from the gods probably because it
    a. enabled agriculture in the middle of a desert.
    b. was the longest river in the world.
    c. was the site of the mighty Aswan High dam.
    d. flowed regularly throughout the year.

17. Settlement of the Sahara is only possible where
    a. cities have grown along river valleys.
    b. mountains provide a buffer against sand storms.
    c. water is available either from springs or deep wells.
    d. little wind or water erosion has taken place.

18. An Islamic fundamentalist would probably be most comfortable living in
    a. Algeria.   b. Tunisia.   c. Morocco.   d. Egypt.

19. The intensive land use brought about by Egypt's rapidly growing population
    a. may make the soil unproductive.
    b. guarantees that enough food will be grown.
    c. means that only cash crops can be grown.
    d. requires every farmer to work harder.

20. As a result of the "Great Manmade River Project,"
    a. the Nile River has been widened to irrigate more farmland.
    b. water is carried from an aquifer in the Sahara to the Libyan coast.
    c. water is shipped from Europe to North Africa through the Suez Canal.
    d. jobs digging irrigation ditches have been provided to workers in Morocco.

Short Answer

Answer the questions in the space provided.

21. How has Libya's oil wealth benefited its people?

    _____
    _____
    _____
    _____
    _____

22. In what areas do most North Africans live? Why?

_____
_____
_____
_____
_____

Critical Thinking

Write your answers on a separate sheet of paper.

23. What kinds of cultural, economic, and/or political ties exist between Europe and the North African countries of Tunisia, Algeria, and Morocco?

24. Islamic fundamentalists encourage a strict, conservative way of life, and are sometimes intolerant of other religious groups. Should they have the right to gain power, or do you agree with several North African governments that have attempted to suppress this movement?

25. Do you think the political power of Muammar al-Qaddafi is related to Libya's oil wealth? Explain.

CHAPTER 36

TEST ANSWERS

Matching

1. Answer: b Objective: 11

2. Answer: e Objective: 11

3. Answer: a Objective: 32

4. Answer: d Objective: 21

5. Answer: f Objective: 11

6. Answer: k Objective: 12

7. Answer: g Objective: 42

8. Answer: j Objective: 41

9. Answer: i Objective: 21

10. Answer: l Objective: 42

Multiple Choice

11. Answer: b Objective: 41

12. Answer: c Objective: 11

13. Answer: a Objective: 22

14. Answer: d Objective: 42

15. Answer: c Objective: 21

16. Answer: a Objective: 12

17. Answer: c Objective: 11

18. Answer: c Objective: 42

19. Answer: a Objective: 21

20. Answer: b Objective: 31

Short Answer

21. Answer:
The government has established public health, housing, and transportation programs, and education and health care have improved. Oil wealth has also funded irrigation projects, such as the "Great Manmade River Project."

Objective: 31

22.Answer:
Most people in North Africa live along the Mediterranean shore, where the climate is suitable for agriculture and where irrigation water is available. Many people also live along the Nile River and in its delta. The largely uninhabitable Sahara covers most of the rest of the region.

Objective: 11

Critical Thinking

23.Answer:
The North African countries of Tunisia, Algeria, and Morocco have close relations with several European nations. Tunisia, a former French colony, still maintains close ties with France. Some Tunisians work in France, and French cultural influences are widely visible in Tunisia. European democratic ideals, such as literacy, quality education, and suffrage for women, are widespread in Tunisia. Many European tourists visit Tunisia's shores.
Algeria was also a French colony. After Algeria won independence, the French infrastructure remained. Algeria trades with the European Community and supplies much of Italy's oil and natural gas.
Morocco is separated from Europe only by the eight-mile (13-km) Strait of Gibraltar. This nearness has encouraged interchange with European countries, and relations are generally friendly. The Moroccan government has allied itself with the United States and western Europe, from whom it receives much foreign aid. The government also encourages cultural exchange and trade with developed countries. Many people of European descent live in Morocco.

Objective: 42

24.Answer:
Answers will vary. Students should address the issue of religious freedom of one group when weighed against the general interests of other groups. Some might argue that if Islamic fundamentalists gain power in North Africa, democratic institutions in the region might be threatened. Other students may suggest that government suppression of people or groups is undemocratic and may backfire or spark a revolution.

Objective: 22

25.Answer:
Possible answer: Much of Qaddafi's power is probably a result of the oil wealth. Libya would have very little influence in the world if it did not control such large oil reserves. Qaddafi would have less success in his military endeavors without the money to support them. Oil wealth also allows Qaddafi to undertake improvements in Libya that gain him support among the population.

Objective: 31

CHAPTER 37

TEST QUESTIONS

Matching

Match the term with its correct description. One term is not used.

a. staple
b. Senegal
c. Niger
d. millet
e. mangrove
f. zonal

1. A country on West Africa's Atlantic coast

2. A landlocked country that was severely affected by the Sahel drought of the 1970s and early 1980s

3. Running in east-west bands, as West Africa's climate regions

4. A drought-resistant grain grown in northern West Africa

5. A main food crop

Match the term with its correct description. One term is not used.

g. sorghum
h. *lingua franca*
i. Sierra Leone
j. pastoralism
k. Guinea-Bissau
l. cassava

6. A language spoken and understood by a majority of people

7. A drought-resistant grain crop grown in northern West Africa

8. An agricultural way of life that involves raising livestock and farming

9. A country that was founded as a settlement for freed slaves

10. A crop whose fleshy, nutritious roots are a source of carbohydrates

Multiple Choice

Circle the letter of the <u>best</u> answer.

11. In most of the Sahel region,
    a. English is the *lingua franca.*
    b. recovery from drought is complete.
    c. mining and manufacturing are the traditional occupations.
    d. refugee settlements surround the capital cities.

12. Of West Africa's three main climate zones, the forest zone is
    a. the driest and most sparsely populated.
    b. the wettest and most densely populated.
    c. the poorest and most mountainous.
    d. the wealthiest and farthest north.

13. The number of ethnic groups living in West Africa is
    a. greater than 2,000.   b. greater than 500.
    c. less than 100.   d. around 20.

14. The traditional occupations in the Sahel region are
    a. fishing and weaving.   b. hunting and gathering.
    c. herding and farming.   d. trading and banking.

15. Few people live in the river valleys of the savanna zone because
    a. overgrazing has led to soil erosion and desertification.
    b. farming is more productive in the drier upland plains.
    c. flies in the region carry diseases.
    d. the climate is too warm.

16. The predominant religion in Senegal, Gambia, and Guinea is
    a. animism.   b. Islam.
    c. Christianity.   d. Creole.

17. All of the following countries are located on West Africa's Guinea coast except
    a. Guinea.   b. Ghana.   c. Togo.   d. Benin.

18. Oil, gold, cacao, and coffee are most important to the economies of the
    a. savanna zone countries.   b. Sahel countries.
    c. Atlantic coast countries.   d. Guinea coast countries.

19. The major cash crop in both Senegal and Gambia is
    a. wheat.   b. peanuts.   c. coffee.   d. bananas.

20. All West African countries
    a. are self-sufficient in food.   b. are still European colonies.
    c. receive foreign aid.   d. have high standards of living.

Short Answer

Answer the questions in the space provided.

21. How did Christianity become an important influence in West Africa?

    _____
    _____
    _____
    _____
    _____

22. Identify the three environmental zones of West Africa. Where is each one located?

    _____
    _____
    _____
    _____
    _____

Critical Thinking

Write your answers on a separate sheet of paper.

23. Why are some countries of West Africa prosperous while others are poor? Give specific examples to support your answer.

24. What role do you think Nigeria's colonial background played in its economic development?

25. Although Liberia was founded as a settlement for freed slaves from the United States, very few African Americans moved there. Why do you think this was?

CHAPTER 37

TEST ANSWERS

Matching

  1.Answer: b Objective: 41

  2.Answer: c Objective: 31

  3.Answer: f Objective: 11

  4.Answer: d Objective: 22

  5.Answer: a Objective: 22

  6.Answer: h Objective: 21

  7.Answer: g Objective: 22

  8.Answer: j Objective: 22

  9.Answer: i Objective: 42

10.Answer: l Objective: 22

Multiple Choice

11.Answer: d Objective: 31

12.Answer: b Objective: 12

13.Answer: b Objective: 21

14.Answer: c Objective: 32

15.Answer: c Objective: 12

16.Answer: b Objective: 42

17.Answer: a Objective: 52

18.Answer: d Objective: 52

19.Answer: b Objective: 41

20.Answer: c Objective: 22

Short Answer

21.Answer:
European traders and explorers in West Africa introduced Christianity
to coastal peoples, and missionaries spread it inland. In some areas, Christianity blended
with animism.

Objective: 21

22.Answer:
   The environmental zones of West Africa are the dryland zone along the southern edge of the Sahara, the wetter savanna zone south of the Sahel, and the forest zone along the West African coast.

   Objective: 11

Critical Thinking

23.Answer:
   Possible answer: A variety of factors can explain why some countries of West Africa have prospered while others have not. Some countries, like Nigeria, are large and have a varied environment that has enabled them to diversify agricultural production. In the Sahel countries, on the other hand, drought has caused continued economic devastation. Mineral wealth is another reason for the prosperity of some West African countries. Nigeria has large oil deposits as well as other minerals. Other countries in the region, however, are not as rich in natural resources.
   Political factors have also played a role in determining countries' economic situations. The prosperity of Cote d'Ivoire and Senegal is related to the stability of these countries' governments. In Guinea, however, a long dictatorship led to increased poverty and economic hardship. The presence of a large population is another factor that has encouraged prosperity in some countries of West Africa, such as Nigeria. Other countries, like drought-stricken Burkina Faso, lose workers who migrate to the coastal countries in search of work.

   Objective: 32

24.Answer:
   Possible answer: The British investment in roads and railroads helped Nigeria develop economically, since the infrastructure necessary for industry was already in place when the country became independent. Yet Nigeria's Muslim kingdoms were prosperous trading centers long before British rule. Furthermore, Nigeria's great mineral wealth might have helped the country prosper regardless of its colonial background. Some students might point out that most West African countries were once colonies but not all are prosperous today.

   Objective: 51

25.Answer:
   Possible answer: Many freed U.S. slaves had been in the United States long enough to consider themselves Americans rather than Africans. In fact, many had even been born in the United States and had never seen Africa. They may have chosen to remain in the United States because it was their home. They may also have believed that the formation of a colony for freed slaves in some way legitimized slavery as an institution.

   Objective: 42

CHAPTER 38

TEST QUESTIONS

Matching

Match the term with its correct description. One term is not used.

a. Kilimanjaro
b. Ethiopian plateau
c. Gezira Scheme
d. gum arabic
e. Eastern Rift
f. sisal

1. A moist climate region in East Africa

2. A strong fiber used to make rope and twine

3. Dry plains in this area are sites of famous game parks

4. An important cash crop of East Africa that comes from the sap of acacia trees

5. An irrigation project in Sudan

Match the term with its correct description. One term is not used.

g. Kikuyu
h. Mogadishu
i. Cushite
j. Zanzibar
k. Rwanda
l. Swahili

6. A language category whose speakers, such as the Amhara and Somali, live from the coast of the Red Sea across the Horn of Africa

7. An island in the Indian Ocean that produces most of the world's cloves

8. A people of Kenya whose ways of life changed drastically during the colonial era

9. A language that has many Arabic words and an African grammar

10. Somalia's capital city

Multiple Choice

Circle the letter of the best answer.

11. The rift valleys are dry because they
    a. are in the rain shadows of mountains.
    b. lie along the equator.
    c. are the continuation of the Sahara in East Africa.
    d. have a high elevation.

12. East Africa can best be described as a region of
    a. rivers and lakes.
    b. high plains and plateaus.
    c. forests and hills.
    d. deserts and basins.

13. Eritrea is
    a. the capital of Tanzania.
    b. the language spoken by most Ugandans.
    c. an Islamic country north of Ethiopia.
    d. a region of farming villages in the highlands of Kenya.

14. Somalia differs from most other African countries in that it
    a. is an industrialized nation with a modern infrastructure.
    b. has very few people who practice Islam.
    c. is populated mainly by a single ethnic group, the Somali.
    d. is ruled by a Communist government.

15. The British and the Kikuyu in Kenya had different ideas about
    a. the use of the Swahili language.
    b. the use of land.
    c. where the railroad should be built.
    d. preserving the mountain gorillas.

16. Most of the people in East Africa work in
    a. commercial farming.
    b. small-scale industry.
    c. building construction.
    d. traditional farming.

17. A difficult political problem facing Sudan is how to
    a. unite the northern Arabs and Nubians with the southern Christians.
    b. gain its independence from Ethiopia.
    c. recover from the effects of Idi Amin's dictatorship.
    d. stop the fighting between the Hutu and Tutsi ethnic groups.

18. The Olduvai Gorge is where
    a. the Eastern Rift and the Western Rift valleys meet.
    b. settlers from Britain built large farms and railways.
    c. most of East Africa's game parks and major cities are located.
    d. evidence of early humanlike settlements has been found.

19. Somalia received aid from other countries in the early 1990s so that it could
    a. build a dam to produce hydroelectric power.
    b. protect itself from invasion by other countries.
    c. recover from civil war and drought.
    d. prevent the spread of desertification.

20. A director making a movie about African game parks would probably do most of the filming in
    a. Ethiopia.   b. Djibouti.   c. Uganda.   d. Kenya.

Short Answer

Answer the questions in the space provided.

21. What cash crops are grown in the drylands of East Africa? in the highlands?

    _____
    _____
    _____
    _____
    _____

22. What was the Mau Mau?

_____
_____
_____
_____
_____

Critical Thinking

Write your answers on a separate sheet of paper.

23. Suppose you were asked by a U.S. business to recommend countries for investment. Which East African countries would you recommend most highly? Which countries would you warn investors away from? Give reasons to support your recommendations.

24. Why do you think the government of Tanzania decided to move the capital from the coastal city of Dar es Salaam to the new inland town of Dodoma?

25. Give an example of how cultural variety affects economic development.

CHAPTER 38

TEST ANSWERS

Matching

1. Answer: b Objective: 12

2. Answer: f Objective: 32

3. Answer: e Objective: 11

4. Answer: d Objective: 22

5. Answer: c Objective: 32

6. Answer: i Objective: 21

7. Answer: j Objective: 31

8. Answer: g Objective: 31

9. Answer: l Objective: 21

10. Answer: h Objective: 42

Multiple Choice

11. Answer: a Objective: 41

12. Answer: b Objective: 11

13. Answer: c Objective: 42

14. Answer: c Objective: 42

15. Answer: b Objective: 31

16. Answer: d Objective: 22

17. Answer: a Objective: 32

18. Answer: d Objective: 31

19. Answer: c Objective: 42

20. Answer: d Objective: 21

Short Answer

21. Answer:
    In the drylands, gum arabic and cotton are major cash crops. Coffee is the most valued cash crop grown in the highlands.
    Objective: 22

22. Answer:

The Mau Mau was a secret guerrilla organization made up of Kikuyu, who were displaced by British settlers during the colonial period. The group protested against British colonial rule after World War II.

Objective: 32

Critical Thinking

23. Answer:

Answers will vary. Students should provide reasons that reflect a weighing of the advantages and disadvantages of investment. Advantages might include mineral wealth (Eritrea, Sudan, Tanzania, Rwanda, Burundi); agricultural potential (Ethiopia, Uganda, Sudan, Rwanda, Burundi); infrastructure and industrial potential (Kenya, Tanzania, Sudan); and stable governments (Kenya, Tanzania). Disadvantages might include political or social unrest (Rwanda, Burundi, Uganda, Sudan, Ethiopia, Somalia, Djibouti); and lack of mineral wealth (Kenya, Somalia) or agricultural potential (Kenya, Tanzania, Somalia). Students should determine what combination of factors would yield the greatest potential for return on investment.

Objective: 42

24. Answer:

Possible answer: Moving the the capital city farther inland might encourage the building of railways and roads in the interior region of the country, thus spreading industrialization throughout the country rather than limiting it to coastal cities. Also, a central location might make the capital more accessible, giving more people a voice in the running of the country.

Objective: 32

25. Answer:

Answers will vary but may discuss how ethnic conflict among culture groups in some countries of East Africa has hindered development in these countries. A possible example includes the conflict in Sudan between the Christians and the Arabs, which has stopped development. Some students may point out that cultural variety does not always interfere with development, as in Djibouti which is evenly split between two groups but is still relatively prosperous.

Objective: 32

CHAPTER 39

TEST QUESTIONS

Matching

Match the term with its correct description. One term is not used.

a. industrial center
b. trust territory
c. Zambezi
d. Malawi
e. periodic market
f. Gabon

1. A river that flows from Zambia to the Indian Ocean

2. A region that is placed under the control of another nation until it can govern itself

3. The most prosperous country in Central Africa

4. A trade and social event held regularly in a town or at a crossroads

5. A landlocked country that receives income from exporting tobacco

Match the term with its correct description. One term is not used.

g. exclave
h. copper
i. Cameroon
j. vanadium
k. Shaba
l. Brazzaville

6. A part of a country that is separated from the rest of the country and is surrounded by foreign territory

7. A mineral-rich region of Zaire

8. A mineral, found in Zambia, that can be combined with iron to make very strong steel

9. A northern Central African country that is nearly self-sufficient in food

10. The capital city of the People's Republic of the Congo

Multiple Choice

Circle the letter of the <u>best</u> answer.

11. Most of Central Africa can best be described as having
    a. plateaus and rolling plains and wet and dry seasons.
    b. dense tropical rain forests and humidity year-round.
    c. desert vegetation and dry conditions year-round.
    d. mountainous highlands and mostly mild climate conditions.

12. The economy of Central Africa is shifting from
    a. industry to manufacturing.
    b. mining to industry.
    c. subsistence agriculture to commercial agriculture.
    d. manufacturing to subsistence agriculture.

13. A major challenge facing Zaire is
    a. improving transportation and communication.
    b. increasing low birthrates.
    c. changing the names of cities back to their colonial names.
    d. resolving the conflict between the Communist government and U.S.-backed rebels.

14. The Central African country that was once a Portuguese colony is
    a. Zaire.   b. Cameroon.   c. Zambia.   d. Angola.

15. In Central Africa today, many workers are
    a. choosing to have smaller families.
    b. looking for work in Asia and Australia.
    c. migrating from rural areas to urban areas to find jobs with cash wages.
    d. establishing periodic markets in large cities.

16. Cameroon is more prosperous than the Central African Republic, in part because
    a. it has a thriving tourist industry.
    b. many of its inhabitants speak French and English.
    c. it has access to foreign aid.
    d. its political leadership is relatively stable.

17. A transportation route essential to the Congo's economy is the
    a. Congo-Ubangi river system.   b. Congo-Ocean Railway.
    c. Trans-Africa Railway.   d. São Tomé and Príncipe Ferry.

18. The resource from which Malawi is most likely to benefit economically in the future is
    a. natural gas.   b. scenery.
    c. vanadium.   d. hydroelectric power.

19. Mountain ranges in Central Africa include the
    a. Adamawa and Mitumba.   b. Zaire and Zambezi.
    c. São Tomé and Príncipe.   d. Kinshasa and Kinsangani.

20. After gaining independence in 1960, Zaire experienced
    a. the rule of a Communist dictator.
    b. exploitation by foreign companies that used forced labor.
    c. a shortage of trained leaders, educators, and medical personnel.
    d. prosperity from developing its enormous manganese reserves.

Short Answer

Answer the questions in the space provided.

21. List three natural resources that could help provide Zaire with a promising future.
    _____
    _____
    _____
    _____
    _____

22. What are Central Africa's main climate types?

_____
_____
_____
_____
_____
_____

Critical Thinking

Write your answers on a separate sheet of paper.

23. In spite of the abundant natural resources and fertile farmland of Central Africa, much of the region has not been prosperous. Explain why this is so, citing specific examples.

24. What special problems are experienced by landlocked countries?

25. If you were a government leader in Angola, what first steps would you take toward solving the problems of the country?

CHAPTER 39

TEST ANSWERS

Matching

1. Answer: c Objective: 11

2. Answer: b Objective: 31

3. Answer: f Objective: 32

4. Answer: e Objective: 12

5. Answer: d Objective: 41

6. Answer: g Objective: 41

7. Answer: k Objective: 22

8. Answer: j Objective: 42

9. Answer: i Objective: 31

10. Answer: l Objective: 31

Multiple Choice

11. Answer: a Objective: 11

12. Answer: c Objective: 12

13. Answer: a Objective: 21

14. Answer: d Objective: 41

15. Answer: c Objective: 12

16. Answer: d Objective: 32

17. Answer: b Objective: 31

18. Answer: b Objective: 42

19. Answer: a Objective: 11

20. Answer: c Objective: 21

Short Answer

21. Answer:
Natural resources include rich mineral wealth (especially copper, oil, and industrial diamonds), a good river system for transporting goods and producing hydroelectricity, an environment suitable for growing commercial crops, and large areas that could be turned into game parks to attract tourists.

Objective: 22

22. Answer:
    Humid-tropical and tropical-savanna climates cover most of Central Africa. Some areas have desert or highland climates.

    Objective: 11

Critical Thinking

23. Answer:
    Possible answer: Poor government policies and political instability have kept Central Africa from reaping the benefits of its rich resources. An example of poor government policy is the encouragement of cash crops to the extent that production of food crops has decreased. In many cases, world and government-controlled prices have been so low that farmers have earned little for their crops. Moreover, food production has not kept up with the rapidly increasing populations in Central Africa, and many countries in the region have had to import food. Struggles with the remnants of a colonial past has kept some countries, such as Zaire, from making economic progress. Civil war and other conflicts, as in Angola, have hindered economic development by draining financial resources—resources that could have been directed toward improving economic and social conditions. Such instability also attracts little foreign investment.

    Objective: 12

24. Answer:
    Landlocked countries often have trouble moving imports and exports. If surrounding countries are experiencing civil war, famine, or other problems, these imports and exports can be blocked, and the economy can suffer. Landlocked countries must work hard to cooperate with governments of other countries.

    Objective: 42

25. Answer:
    Possible answer: Angola's problems include poverty, unemployment, and poor health services. Acquiring capital to improve the social and economic conditions of the country would be an important first step. To do this, the country would need to develop a market for its rich mineral resources by improving relations with the world's industrialized nations. To provide stability and attract foreign capital, Angola would also need to find a complete and final resolution to the conflicts that have plagued the country.

    Objective: 41

CHAPTER 40

TEST QUESTIONS

Matching

Match the term with its correct description. One term is not used.

a. sanctions
b. Boers
c. homelands
d. copra
e. veld
f. Namibia

1. The dried meat of the coconut, from which coconut oil is obtained

2. Economic measures taken by nations to force another nation to cease illegal or immoral actions

3. A term used to describe South Africa's various natural regions

4. European settlers in Southern Africa, who became frontier farmers

5. South African territories in which blacks were given citizenship whether they lived there or not

Match the term with its correct description. One term is not used.

g. exile
h. Soweto
i. Kariba
j. Witwatersrand
k. embargo
l. apartheid

6. A site on the Zambezi River where hydroelectricity is generated

7. A legal restriction against the movement of freight

8. A series of laws intended to separate the different ethnic groups of South Africa

9. A person who has been forced to leave his or her country

10. The largest industrial region on the African continent

Multiple Choice

Circle the letter of the best answer.

11. Unlike Namibia and Botswana, Mozambique and Madagascar are most likely to earn future income from
    a. tourism rather than agriculture.
    b. agriculture rather than mining.
    c. fishing rather than manufacturing.
    d. manufacturing rather than services.

12. In Southern Africa, the savanna region of short trees that is found at lower elevations is called the
    a. bushveld.   b. highveld.   c. woodveld.   d. lowveld.

13. Although apartheid is disappearing in South Africa,
    a. no white schools have yet accepted black students.
    b. black and white neighborhoods are still generally segregated.
    c. there is still no contact among the races.
    d. most public facilities are still segregated.

14. South Africa's wealth is based primarily on its
    a. mineral reserves.   b. oil wells.
    c. military strength.   d. homelands policy.

15. A country that received its independence from South Africa in 1990 is
    a. Botswana.   b. Mozambique.
    c. Madagascar.   d. Namibia.

16. The Anglo-Boer War was fought in part because of
    a. South Africa's policy of apartheid.
    b. disagreements about black land ownership.
    c. the Boers' distrust of British expansion.
    d. the loyalty of many Afrikaners to Europe.

17. The South African government reacted to the African National Congress's 1950s protests against apartheid by
    a. desegregating all public facilities, schools, and neighborhoods.
    b. banning the African National Congress and jailing its leaders.
    c. declaring the homelands independent countries.
    d. placing embargoes on products made by African National Congress members.

18. Under apartheid, blacks in South Africa
    a. occupied a social status between whites and coloureds.
    b. received good educations but remained largely unemployed.
    c. were denied political influence and had little access to economic opportunities.
    d. were legally represented in the government only by the African National Congress.

19. The principal economic activities in Botswana are
    a. mining and cattle herding.   b. tourism and commercial farming.
    c. manufacturing and fishing.   d. logging and hunting.

20. In Zimbabwe today,
    a. most of the commercial farms are owned by blacks.
    b. a network of irrigation canals is being built to support small farms.
    c. the country's large farms always provide enough food for export.
    d. the government is trying to give blacks and whites equal shares of farmland.

Short Answer

Answer the questions in the space provided.

21. What is the Drakensberg Escarpment, and where is it located?

_____
_____
_____
_____
_____
_____

22. Why is the Okavango Delta important to Botswana?

_____
_____
_____
_____
_____
_____

Critical Thinking

Write your answers on a separate sheet of paper.

23. Summarize the history of apartheid in South Africa.

24. How do you think the end of apartheid as a government policy will affect the economy of South Africa?

25. Is it fair for countries to use sanctions against nations that abuse human rights? Why or why not?

CHAPTER 40

TEST ANSWERS

Matching

1. Answer: d Objective: 32

2. Answer: a Objective: 22

3. Answer: e Objective: 11

4. Answer: b Objective: 12

5. Answer: c Objective: 21

6. Answer: i Objective: 11

7. Answer: k Objective: 22

8. Answer: l Objective: 21

9. Answer: g Objective: 22

10. Answer: j Objective: 23

Multiple Choice

11. Answer: b Objective: 31

12. Answer: a Objective: 11

13. Answer: b Objective: 21

14. Answer: a Objective: 23

15. Answer: d Objective: 31

16. Answer: c Objective: 12

17. Answer: b Objective: 22

18. Answer: c Objective: 21

19. Answer: a Objective: 32

20. Answer: d Objective: 32

Short Answer

21. Answer:

The Drakensberg Escarpment is an escarpment, or steep slope capped by a plateau, that runs along the coast of the Indian Ocean in Southern Africa. From the eastern side, the escarpment looks like a mountain; the western side, however, forms the edge of a region of high plains.

Objective: 11

22. Answer:
Rich wetland forests and large game reserves are located in this delta. Someday, these wetlands could be a major tourist attraction generating income for the country.

Objective: 32

Critical Thinking

23. Answer:
Apartheid, a policy of separation of races and ethnic groups in South Africa, was established by South Africa's white-run government after the 1948 elections. Under this policy, blacks, Asians, and coloureds (people of mixed race) were forced by law to live, work, and go to school separately from white people. The country's blacks were assigned to territories, or homelands, based on ethnic groups. Under the homelands policy, black South Africans were given citizenship in the homeland of their ethnic group, whether they lived there or not. Thus, many blacks officially became foreigners with few civil rights in the places outside their official homeland The homelands, meanwhile, had limited development, medical care, and educational opportunities.

Many countries were opposed to South Africa's policy of apartheid. In 1961, South Africa was forced to leave the British Commonwealth. Some sports teams and products were boycotted by other countries. Embargoes and sanctions were placed on South African products to force the nation to stop apartheid. Within South Africa, the African National Congress and other organizations disobeyed apartheid laws and were violently suppressed.

In 1989, apartheid, which had not worked economically and had caused serious problems for South Africa around the world, began to disappear as official government policy. Relations with the ANC were reopened, apartheid laws were repealed, and jailed leaders, including Nelson Mandela, were released. Slowly, integration has been taking place in South Africa, although relations between the races remain strained.

Objective: 21

24. Answer:
Possible answer: Now that apartheid has ended, embargoes and other economic sanctions against South Africa are being lifted. As a result, foreign countries will be more likely to purchase goods produced in South Africa, having a positive effect on the economy. Also, allowing a large part of the population—the people who were held back under apartheid—to participate fully in the society may help the economy. Political instability during a time of transition, however, might create economic uncertainty in the short run.

Objective: 23

25. Answer:
Answers will vary. Students should consider how sanctions affect the economic well-being of some of the very people whose rights the foreign countries are trying to protect. In addition, sanctions are not always effective in bringing about change. Students who support sanctions, however, will probably argue that long-term benefits outweigh short-term suffering.

Objective: 22

UNIT 8

TEST QUESTIONS

Matching

Match the term with its correct description. One term is not used.

a. Kalahari
b. Gambia
c. rift
d. Swahili
e. escarpment
f. Kenya

1. A narrow trough, or valley, with mountainous slopes on each side

2. A desert in Southern Africa with some low grasses and shrubs

3. A steep slope capped by a nearly flat plateau

4. The common language of East Africa

5. A West African country almost entirely surrounded by the country of Senegal

Match the term with its correct description. One term is not used.

g. bushveld
h. Atlas
i. Sahel
j. embargo
k. apartheid
l. Kush

6. A savanna region found at lower elevations in South Africa

7. The dry savanna region along the southern edge of the Sahara

8. The recently repealed South African policy of separation of the races

9. A mountain range located along part of the North African coast

10. An ancient kingdom that once controlled much of the middle Nile River valley

Multiple Choice

Circle the letter of the best answer.

11. Many early African empires grew powerful by controlling
    a. European expansion on the continent.
    b. trade routes across Africa.
    c. Asian colonies on the Indian Ocean coast.
    d. the spread of the Sahel region.

12. As a result of the boundaries drawn by Europeans, many African nations
    a. refuse to trade with European countries today.
    b. rely more on commercial agriculture than subsistence agriculture.
    c. are landlocked and experience conflict among ethnic groups.
    d. chose to redraw those boundaries when they gained independence.

13. Drought is an especially serious problem in West Africa because much of the region
    a. has limited irrigation potential.
    b. does not receive foreign aid to build irrigation canals.
    c. is located in a climate zone where rainfall is unreliable.
    d. has a relatively small population.

14. Many African countries are experiencing
    a. the migration of workers from rural areas to overcrowded cities.
    b. the potential for flooding in much of the Sahel region.
    c. environmental pollution caused by industrialization.
    d. falling birthrates and rising death rates.

15. The period in which most African countries gained independence from European rule was
    a. 1980 to 1990.   b. 1865 to 1875.
    c. 1955 to 1965.   d. 1930 to 1940.

16. Large quantities of copper, vanadium, and coffee are all produced in
    a. East Africa.   b. West Africa.
    c. Southern Africa.   d. Central Africa.

17. Nigeria has often assumed a leadership role in much of Africa because of its
    a. large population and oil wealth.
    b. highly industrialized society.
    c. lack of ethnic and religious conflict.
    d. status within the United Nations.

18. The Eastern Rift Valley passes through
    a. Gabon and Guinea.   b. Libya and Egypt.
    c. Tanzania and Kenya.   d. Botswana and Zaire.

19. The country that was once called the Belgian Congo is
    a. Zaire.
    b. Burkina Faso.
    c. the People's Republic of the Congo.
    d. Zimbabwe.

20. In South Africa today,
    a. most blacks live in the homeland of their ethnic group.
    b. the Zulus and the Xhosas have resolved their cultural and political differences.
    c. apartheid has been repealed, but race relations are still tense.
    d. the economy has not been affected by the struggle over apartheid.

Short Answer

Answer the questions in the space provided.

21. What major religions are practiced in Africa?
    _____
    _____
    _____
    _____
    _____

22. Why can a wide variety of crops be grown in Africa?

_____

_____

_____

_____

_____

Critical Thinking

Write your answers on a separate sheet of paper.

23. Which region of the African continent do you think has the best chance for development in the next century? To support your answer, compare this region's political, social, and economic conditions with those of other African regions.

24. Could the South African policy of apartheid have developed in other countries of Africa? Why or why not?

25. How might African nations reduce the amount of food they import?

UNIT 8

TEST ANSWERS

Matching

1.Answer: c Objective: 81

2.Answer: a Objective: 81

3.Answer: e Objective: 81

4.Answer: d Objective: 85

5.Answer: b Objective: 81

6.Answer: g Objective: 81

7.Answer: i Objective: 81

8.Answer: k Objective: 84

9.Answer: h Objective: 81

10.Answer: l Objective: 82

Multiple Choice

11.Answer: b Objective: 82

12.Answer: c Objective: 84

13.Answer: c Objective: 81

14.Answer: a Objective: 84

15.Answer: c Objective: 82

16.Answer: d Objective: 83

17.Answer: a Objective: 83

18.Answer: c Objective: 81

19.Answer: a Objective: 82

20.Answer: c Objective: 84

Short Answer

21.Answer:
Major religions practiced in Africa include Islam and Christianity. Many people also practice animism, a traditional belief in nature and spiritual beings.

Objective: 85

22. Answer:
    Africa is a large continent, stretching some 5,000 miles (8,045 km) from north to south across many degrees of latitude. The continent has several climate types, each of which supports the growth of different types of crops.

    Objective: 83

Critical Thinking

23. Answer:
    Answers will vary. Students should consider the reasons for the slow development of many countries in Africa, including political and social unrest, poor government economic policies, poor physical conditions, rapid population growth, and dependence on foreign aid. They should evaluate the physical geography, natural resources, and political and social situations in each region to determine which one is best equipped to face the challenges of development. For example, students who choose Central Africa might recognize that the region has substantial agricultural and mineral resources and that many of the region's countries are increasingly politically stable.

    Objective: 83

24. Answer:
    Possible answer: Probably not. The historical development of most of Africa has been different from that of South Africa. Unlike other regions of the continent where African leaders took over colonial governments after independence, an economically and politically influential European-descended minority settled in South Africa and remained there even after independence from Great Britain. A system of separation of the races was implemented in South Africa because the white minority had tremendous power over the black majority. This has not been the case in most other African countries.

    Objective: 85

25. Answer:
    Possible answer: African nations could reduce their dependence on the export of cash crops and place more emphasis on the growing of food crops for domestic use. They could develop industry, mineral resources, and tourist potential to compensate for the lack of income from cash crops. Furthermore, they might increase their productivity through the use of more effective farming practices and by developing water resources to expand irrigation use in areas with unreliable rainfall. Farming involving a combination of cash crops and food crops also might be introduced.

    Objective: 84

CHAPTER 41

TEST QUESTIONS

Matching

Match the term with its correct description. One term is not used.

a. alluvial
b. Tian Shan
c. Shinto
d. paddy
e. Huang He
f. pictogram

1. Simple pictures of ideas and objects, like some Chinese characters

2. A water-covered field, often used to raise rice

3. A religion practiced in Japan based on the worship of nature gods

4. A mountain range that separates northwestern China from Russia

5. One of the world's longest rivers, located in northern China

Match the term with its correct description. One term is not used.

g. Confucianism
h. Buddhism
i. tungsten
j. aquaculture
k. Taoism
l. typhoon

6. A code of ethics based on the teachings of a Chinese philosopher

7. Farming in seas and ponds

8. A religion founded in India around 500 B.C., whose followers seek enlightenment through meditation

9. A religion whose followers seek harmony by attempting to live a simple life close to nature

10. A mineral used in the production of electronics and lighting materials

Multiple Choice

Circle the letter of the best answer.

11. Increased industrialization in parts of East and Southeast Asia has led to
    a. urban crowding and water and air pollution.
    b. border disputes and an increasing refugee population in some nations.
    c. full development of oil and hydroelectricity potential.
    d. decreased competition among countries in the region.

12. The region's major economic power and the world's second leading industrial country is
    a. Singapore.   b. Indonesia.   c. China.   d. Japan.

13. Singapore, Taiwan, Hong Kong, and South Korea are known as
    a. agricultural countries.
    b. environmentally sensitive countries.
    c. newly industrialized countries.
    d. Communist countries.

14. Few people inhabit the plateaus between Asia's mountains because these regions
    a. experience severe flooding during the monsoons.
    b. are dry with very cold winters.
    c. are so high that they lack sufficient oxygen for human life.
    d. fall below sea level and are very hot.

15. East and Southeast Asia has large reserves of all of the following except
    a. tin.   b. tungsten.   c. bauxite.   d. oil.

16. East and Southeast Asia's political geography can be described as
    a. varied.   b. democratic.   c. Communist.   d. military.

17. Many East and Southeast Asian islands that are part of the Pacific Ring of Fire
    a. experience natural forest fires on a regular basis.
    b. are volcanic and were formed by tectonic activity.
    c. do not support human settlements because of poor soils.
    d. are agriculturally productive only with slash-and-burn farming.

18. To unify their diverse peoples, some East and Southeast Asian countries, such as China and Indonesia, have
    a. adopted one official language.
    b. outlawed the worship of nature gods.
    c. moved their capitals to central locations.
    d. required that their citizens practice Buddhism.

19. Annual rainfall in East and Southeast Asia is
    a. high throughout the region.
    b. high in some areas and low in others.
    c. distributed evenly throughout the year in most areas.
    d. concentrated mainly in the winter.

20. Two threatened resources in East and Southeast Asia are
    a. fish and forests.   b. gold and oil.
    c. soil and water.   d. air and coal.

Short Answer

Answer the questions in the space provided.

21. What factors affect population distribution patterns in East and Southeast Asia?

    _____

    _____

    _____

    _____

    _____

22. How have many countries in East and Southeast Asia been changing economically in recent years?

_____
_____
_____
_____
_____
_____

Critical Thinking

Write your answers on a separate sheet of paper.

23. Summarize the political history of East and Southeast Asia over the past three centuries.

24. Compare and contrast Shinto and Taoism. Consider their basic beliefs, origins, and where they are practiced.

25. Many pictograms are common in daily life in the United States. List three pictograms that you see on a regular basis. What advantages might a pictogram have over a spelled-out word?

CHAPTER 41

TEST ANSWERS

Matching

1. Answer: f Objective: 31

2. Answer: d Objective: 21

3. Answer: c Objective: 31

4. Answer: b Objective: 11

5. Answer: e Objective: 11

6. Answer: g Objective: 31

7. Answer: j Objective: 21

8. Answer: h Objective: 31

9. Answer: k Objective: 31

10. Answer: i Objective: 21

Multiple Choice

11. Answer: a Objective: 22

12. Answer: d Objective: 22

13. Answer: c Objective: 22

14. Answer: b Objective: 12

15. Answer: c Objective: 21

16. Answer: a Objective: 32

17. Answer: b Objective: 11

18. Answer: a Objective: 31

19. Answer: b Objective: 11

20. Answer: a Objective: 21

Short Answer

21. Answer:
Climate is a major factor affecting population distribution patterns. Because much of the land of the region is mountainous, dry, and cold, most of the people have settled in milder areas such as valleys, deltas, coastal plains, and interior plains. In addition, many people live near rivers, which provide rich new soil for farming when they are flooded and are important for irrigation and transportation.

Objective: 12

22.Answer:
   Many countries of the region, such as Taiwan, Singapore, Hong Kong, and South Korea, have undergone rapid industrialization. These newly industrialized countries have experienced explosive economic growth, and their economies are very competitive.

   Objective: 22

Critical Thinking

23.Answer:
   Possible answer: Many parts of East and Southeast Asia were colonized by foreign powers during the eighteenth and nineteenth centuries. Britain, the Netherlands, France, Portugal, Spain, and the United States all had colonies in the region. Japan, another colonizer in the region, gained control of much of East and Southeast Asia during World War II. After World War II, most of the countries in the region sought independence. The new nations of the Philippines, Indonesia, Burma, Vietnam, Cambodia, and Laos were established.
   Several conflicts marked the region in the decades following World War II. After a civil war in China, Communists established the People's Republic of China in 1949. Taiwan was formed on an island off mainland China at this time by the Nationalists, opponents of the Communists. Korea became a battleground for South Korean, U.S., and United Nations forces in a struggle against North Korea and China. The Vietnam War, which involved a struggle of South Vietnamese and U.S. forces against the North Vietnamese, ended with the unification of North and South Vietnam under a Communist government.
   Today, political systems vary widely in East and Southeast Asia—some countries are democratic, some are Communist, some are military dictatorships, some remain colonies. Political tension still characterizes much of the region as a result of the internal conflicts and disputes among some of the countries.

   Objective: 32

24.Answer:
   Possible answer: Shinto and Taoism both emphasize nature. Shintoists worship nature gods through a loosely structured set of rituals at local shrines, and Taoists attempt to live a simple life close to nature and to be in harmony with the *Tao*, the natural order of the universe. Neither Taoism nor Shinto claim to have been revealed by a god. The two religions differ, however, in that Taoism was founded by a philosopher named Lao-Tzu, while Shinto does not claim to have any founder at all. Taoism is practiced mainly in China; Shinto is practiced in Japan.

   Objective: 31

25.Answer:
   Examples of pictograms common in the United States will vary but might include stick figures for men and women, symbols found on traffic or highway signs, or simple drawings on warning labels of household products (such as to indicate "poison.") One advantage of pictograms over spelled-out words might be that pictograms can be understood by people who do not read English. Another possible advantage is that pictograms can be observed and understood quickly, as by people driving by in cars who are going too fast to stop to read words or sentences.

   Objective: 31

CHAPTER 42

TEST QUESTIONS

Matching

Match the term with its correct description. One term is not used.

a. Mao Zedong
b. Silk Road
c. Shanghai
d. Hong Kong
e. Chiang Kai-shek
f. Chang Delta

1. China's Nationalist leader who came to power in 1925 and attempted to weaken the Communist influence in China

2. A British colony that will return to Chinese control in 1997

3. A trade route that connected China with Central Asia and Europe

4. China's Communist leader who came to power in 1949 and attempted to restructure the country economically and socially

5. One of China's major rice-growing regions

Match the term with its correct description. One term is not used.

g. puppet government
h. town village enterprise
i. commune
j. terracing
k. dynasty
l. martial law

6. A political system that is controlled by outside forces

7. A government ruled by a family over a long period of time through many generations

8. A form of military rule, such as that experienced by Taiwan for almost 40 years

9. A large cooperative group of agricultural workers

10. Building rice paddies at different levels along hillsides

Multiple Choice

Circle the letter of the <u>best</u> answer.

11. Special Economic Zones (SEZs)
    a. are rural and village areas with many small, privately owned companies.
    b. were formed along the coast of southern China to attract foreign investment.
    c. were established by Mao Zedong as part of the Cultural Revolution.
    d. arose as urban centers along the early trade routes between China and Europe.

12. The Mongol invasion of China led by Genghis Khan took place
    a. after the decline of the Ming dynasty but before the building of the Great Wall.
    b. after Chinese culture expanded into southern China but before the decline of the Manchu dynasty.
    c. after the Chinese style of writing developed but before the Qin dynasty came to power.
    d. after the Opium War broke out but before many Chinese emigrated to the United States and Canada.

13. Taiwan is a world leader in the production of
    a. wheat, millet, and corn.
    b. computers, calculators, and scientific instruments.
    c. automobiles, trucks, and buses.
    d. silk, cotton textiles, and carpets.

14. Double cropping is made possible in southern China by
    a. wind-blown deposits of rich yellow-brown soil called loess.
    b. the heavy flooding of the Chang and Xi rivers during winter months.
    c. the region's humid-subtropical climate, which provides a long growing season.
    d. the terracing of hillsides, which increases the amount of area available for cultivation.

15. Manchuria and Inner Mongolia are both located in
    a. southern China.   b. Tibet.
    c. northeastern China.   d. Outer Mongolia.

16. The Mongolian economy has declined partly as a result of
    a. the collapse of the Soviet Union.
    b. free elections held in 1990.
    c. the depletion of its natural resources.
    d. Mongolia's independence from Great Britain.

17. During China's Han dynasty,
    a. Chinese culture flourished and expanded into southern China.
    b. China was divided and ruled by numerous warlords.
    c. irrigation agriculture was developed along the Huang He.
    d. China isolated itself from other cultures.

18. During the Cultural Revolution,
    a. Nationalist and Communist forces battled for control of mainland China.
    b. Mao attempted to improve the economy by setting fixed agricultural and industrial goals.
    c. farmers organized themselves into collectives and donated their private land to the government.
    d. the government suppressed education and urged everyone to follow the peasant way of life.

19. If a silk scarf sold in an American department store is marked "Made in China," it was most likely produced in the city of
    a. Shanghai.   b. T'aipei.   c. Ürümqi.   d. Ulaanbaatar.

20. China's capital and northern China's largest city is
    a. Shanghai.   b. Hong Kong.   c. Chonquing.   d. Beijing.

Short Answer

Answer the questions in the space provided.

21. When was Christianity introduced into China, and by whom?

_____
_____
_____
_____
_____

22. Explain why western China, which covers more than one-third of the nation's territory, has such a small population.

_____
_____
_____
_____
_____

Critical Thinking

Write your answers on a separate sheet of paper.

23. How does China's economy today compare to what it was in the 1960s and 1970s?

24. Predict what the relationship between Taiwan and China will be like by the year 2020.

25. If you were the head of a growing business enterprise in the United States, would you recommend investment in Mongolia? Why or why not?

CHAPTER 42

TEST ANSWERS

Matching

1. Answer: e Objective: 11

2. Answer: d Objective: 22

3. Answer: b Objective: 11

4. Answer: a Objective: 12

5. Answer: f Objective: 21

6. Answer: g Objective: 11

7. Answer: k Objective: 11

8. Answer: l Objective: 31

9. Answer: i Objective: 12

10. Answer: j Objective: 21

Multiple Choice

11. Answer: b Objective: 21

12. Answer: b Objective: 11

13. Answer: b Objective: 31

14. Answer: c Objective: 21

15. Answer: c Objective: 21

16. Answer: a Objective: 32

17. Answer: a Objective: 11

18. Answer: d Objective: 12

19. Answer: a Objective: 22

20. Answer: d Objective: 22

Short Answer

21. Answer:
Christianity was introduced into China by European missionaries after the first Portuguese trading colony was established at Macao in 1557.
Objective: 11

22.Answer:
   The region's physical geography has discouraged extensive development. The mountainous country is too high, cold, and dry to support a large population.

   Objective: 21

Critical Thinking

23.Answer:
   Possible answer: Under the leadership of Mao Zedong, China experienced economic hardship. During the Great Leap Forward, instituted in 1958, the government set agricultural and industrial quotas rather than look to the market needs of the people. All private land was seized and people were forced to work on communes. The program forced people to work harder without reward, delayed economic development, caused starvation, and was an environmental disaster.
   Since the death of Mao in 1976, a new leadership under Deng Xiaoping has admitted the failure of Mao's policies and has initiated a new policy to modernize agriculture, industry, and technology in China. Farmers are no longer organized in communes, but rather are allowed to grow and market their own crops. China is now almost self-sufficient in food. Private enterprise and self-employment are growing, although state-owned industry is still a major employer. Town village enterprises (TVEs), small companies based in rural areas, are the fastest growing sector of China's economy. More consumer products are now available to the Chinese. Special Economic Zones (SEZs) have been established to encourage foreign investment in China. Although political freedoms are still limited in China, economic freedoms and prosperity have increased since the 1960s and 1970s.

   Objective: 12

24.Answer:
   Possible answer: As China's economy advances and economic differences between the two countries lessen, there will probably be more trade and increased economic interdependence between them. These economic ties may bring opportunities for cultural and political exchanges as well. Eventually, China and Taiwan may reunify.

   Objective: 31

25.Answer:
   Answers will vary. Some students may say that Mongolia's mineral resources, such as coal, copper, and oil, might be further developed to yield a healthy return. Other students might say that the country's current economic situation, isolation and landlocked location, and unpredictable physical conditions would make it too much of a risk for investment.

   Objective: 32

CHAPTER 43

TEST QUESTIONS

Matching

Match the term with its correct description. One term is not used.

a. trade surplus
b. annex
c. Seoul
d. work ethic
e. Honshu
f. export economy

1. To formally join one country or region to another

2. An economic imbalance that arises when a nation exports more than it imports

3. Japan's largest and most populated island

4. A production policy that favors manufacturing products for sale to other nations

5. A belief, held by many Japanese, that labor is good in and of itself

Match the term with its correct description. One term is not used.

g. subsidy
h. typhoon
i. urban agglomeration
j. tsunami
k. *shogun*
l. demilitarized zone (DMZ)

6. A Japanese military leader of the pre-modernization era

7. A large sea wave caused by tectonic activity

8. A two-and-a-half-mile-wide border between North and South Korea

9. A densely inhabited and contiguous region surrounding a central city

10. Financial support given by a government

Multiple Choice

Circle the letter of the <u>best</u> answer.

11. If you looked at a map of Japan and Korea, at about 38 degrees north latitude you would find the
    a. river that separates the Korean Peninsula from China.
    b. border between North Korea and South Korea.
    c. strait between the islands of Honshu and Hokkaido.
    d. border between North Korea and Russia.

12. During the Meiji Restoration,
    a. the Ainu were driven north by Mongoloid invaders from Asia.
    b. Japan modernized its economy, educational system, and government.
    c. Spanish and Portuguese missionaries introduced Christianity to Japan.
    d. Japan patterned its writing system and religious customs after the Chinese.

13. Today, some of Japan's most aggressive competition comes from
    a. American agribusiness.
    b. former Soviet republics.
    c. African industries.
    d. newly industrialized Asian countries.

14. More people live in South Korea than in North Korea, in part because
    a. fewer South Koreans than North Koreans were killed during the Korean War.
    b. the mountainous terrain of South Korea supports large populations.
    c. the humid-subtropical climate and flat land in the south allow more agricultural
       development.
    d. South Korea's Communist government will not allow its citizens to leave the country.

15. Both Japan and South Korea
    a. produce coal and iron ore but import fruits.
    b. export hardwoods and softwoods but import electronics.
    c. prohibit private ownership of farms and businesses but rely on foreign labor.
    d. raise rice and fish but import oil.

16. Most Koreans live
    a. on the coastal plain along the peninsula's western coast.
    b. in the peninsula's northeastern mountainous region.
    c. along the banks of the Yalu River.
    d. on the island of Hokkaido.

17. Two characteristics of the Japanese population are
    a. traditional roles for women and a small middle class.
    b. a low birthrate and a high life expectancy.
    c. shrinking urban areas and a limited work ethic.
    d. a large upper class and low literacy rates.

18. Urban Japanese experience all of the following except
    a. air pollution.   b. expensive housing.
    c. high crime rates.   d. traffic congestion.

19. More than 70 percent of Japan consists of
    a. deserts.   b. mountains.
    c. grasslands.   d. wetlands.

20. All of the following are trade or industrial centers of Japan except
    a. Tokyo.   b. Osaka.   c. P'yongyang.   d. Nagoya.

Short Answer

Answer the questions in the space provided.

21. Why is Japan subject to frequent earthquakes and volcanic eruptions?
    _____
    _____
    _____
    _____
    _____

22. Identify the climate regions of Japan and the Korean Peninsula.

_____
_____
_____
_____
_____

Critical Thinking

Write your answers on a separate sheet of paper.

23. What factors have enabled Japan to become such a technological and industrial success?

24. Japanese crop yields are some of the highest in the world, yet Japan imports about half its food. Why?

25. What might Korea be like today had the Korean War ended with reunification?

CHAPTER 43

TEST ANSWERS

Matching

1. Answer: b Objective: 11

2. Answer: a Objective: 12

3. Answer: e Objective: 11

4. Answer: f Objective: 22

5. Answer: d Objective: 12

6. Answer: k Objective: 11

7. Answer: j Objective: 11

8. Answer: l Objective: 22

9. Answer: i Objective: 13

10. Answer: g Objective: 12

Multiple Choice

11. Answer: b Objective: 22

12. Answer: b Objective: 11

13. Answer: d Objective: 12

14. Answer: c Objective: 22

15. Answer: d Objective: 12

16. Answer: a Objective: 21

17. Answer: b Objective: 13

18. Answer: c Objective: 13

19. Answer: b Objective: 11

20. Answer: c Objective: 13

Short Answer

21. Answer:
    Japan lies along a subduction zone, where the Eurasian and Philippine plates overlap the
    Pacific plate. The movement of these plates causes frequent earthquakes, volcanic
    activity, and tsunami, or large waves.

    Objective: 11

22. Answer:

Both Japan and the Korean Peninsula have humid-continental climate regions in the north and humid-subtropical climate regions in the south.

Objective: 21

Critical Thinking

23. Answer:

Possible answer: Japan had a relatively early start on modernization during its Meiji period, and by the early twentieth century it was recognized as a world power. After the devastation caused by World War II, with U.S. aid Japan was able to rebuild itself as a major world industrial power. Today, Japan produces goods whose quality is rated highly around the world. The keys to Japan's economic success lie largely in its culture and its people. The fact that nearly everyone in Japan is of Japanese origin makes communication and the setting of common goals easier. Furthermore, Japan's people have a strong work ethic, and employees and employers generally have good relationships. Japanese workers often participate in corporate decision making, and most workers are loyal to their companies. Japan's people also are generally well educated and are familiar with the markets and nations that buy their exported products. The Japanese themselves are major consumers of Japanese industrial products, ensuring a home market to test new products. Finally, the Japanese government works closely with Japanese businesses, offering financial aid and import protection.

Objective: 12

24. Answer:

Possible answer: Japan is quite mountainous and has very little arable land. Although terraced cultivation and modern farming methods enable Japan to maximize the use of its arable land, giving the country high crop yields, these yields are not sufficient to feed Japan's large population—a population over four times that of California, a U.S. state that has five times as much land area as Japan. Furthermore, Japan's terrain and climates cannot support the growth of all types of crops. Japan must import all types of food, particularly grains and meats, that it cannot raise itself in large quantities. Food imports have also increased as Western foods have become more popular in Japan.

Objective: 12

25. Answer:

Answers will vary. Some students may say that a reunified government would probably have been unstable, given the two regions' political differences. Students might also hypothesize about the economic consequences of reunification: If Korea had been reunified under a Communist government like that currently existing in North Korea, then South Korea might not have become an economic power. On the other hand, if Korea had been reunified under a democratic government like that currently existing in South Korea, the entire peninsula might have progressed economically. The resources of northern Korea might have reduced the need to import raw materials for development.

Objective: 22

CHAPTER 44

TEST QUESTIONS

Matching

Match the term with its correct description. One term is not used.

a. Irrawaddy
b. defoliant
c. manganese
d. Indonesia
e. teak
f. Thailand

1. A former Dutch colony of Southeast Asia

2. The Southeast Asian country that stretches from the central part of the mainland south to the Malay Peninsula

3. A chemical, such as that used by U.S. forces during the Vietnam War, that makes plants' leaves drop off

4. An important river that flows through Burma

5. An evergreen tree whose wood is valued for furniture making

Match the term with its correct description. One term is not used.

g. intensive agriculture
h. Phnom Penh
i. double cropping
j. Chao Phraya
k. Khmer Rouge
l. shifting agriculture

6. Farming that uses much human labor, such as the raising of rice

7. A large, important river in Thailand

8. Communist forces that held power in Cambodia from 1975 to 1978

9. The capital city of Cambodia

10. Farming in which farmers periodically move to new areas, often as a result of slash-and-burn techniques that deplete the soil

Multiple Choice

Circle the letter of the <u>best</u> answer.

11. A group of people who migrated to Southeast Asia before the growth of the Khmer Empire were the
    a. Burmese.   b. Thais.   c. Arabs.   d. Koreans.

12. The climates of Southeast Asia are
   a. humid tropical and tropical savanna.
   b. humid continental and humid subtropical.
   c. highland and steppe.
   d. marine west coast and Mediterranean.

13. Burma's political system is a
   a. democracy.
   c. military government.
   b. Communist state.
   d. constitutional monarchy.

14. The countries of Vietnam, Cambodia, and Laos were once part of
   a. French Indochina.
   c. Indonesia.
   b. Singapore.
   d. the Philippines.

15. The Mekong River
   a. is the major river of the Philippines.
   b. flows from the Himalayas to the Plateau of Tibet.
   c. borders Thailand and flows through Laos, Cambodia, and Vietnam.
   d. flows through Burma and Thailand.

16. All of the following are ethnic groups of Southeast Asia except
   a. Montagnards.
   c. Hmong.
   b. Klongs.
   d. Lao.

17. With the exception of Thailand, all of Southeast Asia was
   a. invaded by Cambodia during the Vietnam War.
   b. conquered by Japan during World War I.
   c. once colonized by European powers.
   d. independent at the start of World War II.

18. During the Vietnam War, supply lines to the North Vietnamese were bombed in
   a. Russia and China.
   c. Thailand and Burma.
   b. Malaysia and Indonesia.
   d. Laos and Cambodia.

19. The most valuable commercial crop in Southeast Asia is
   a. rubber.   b. bananas.   c. cassava.   d. beans.

20. Thailand's economy has grown rapidly, in part as a result of
   a. independence from Great Britain.
   b. foreign investment.
   c. a Communist government.
   d. peaceful relations between Thailand and neighboring Cambodia and Laos.

Short Answer

Answer the questions in the space provided.

21. Identify the three landform regions of Southeast Asia.

   _____
   _____
   _____
   _____
   _____

22. What factors made Southeast Asia an ideal site for European-owned plantations?

   _____
   _____
   _____
   _____
   _____

Critical Thinking

Write your answers on a separate sheet of paper.

23. How is Southeast Asia important to the world economy? What major economic challenges face the region?

24. Agree or disagree with the following statement: "The conflicts in mainland Southeast Asia have all been a part of the world conflict between Communist countries and non-Communist countries."

25. Why do you think the United States does not recognize the name of Southeast Asia's westernmost country as Myanmar?

CHAPTER 44

TEST ANSWERS

Matching

1. Answer: d Objective: 12

2. Answer: f Objective: 21

3. Answer: b Objective: 21

4. Answer: a Objective: 11

5. Answer: e Objective: 12

6. Answer: g Objective: 12

7. Answer: j Objective: 11

8. Answer: k Objective: 22

9. Answer: h Objective: 21

10. Answer: l Objective: 12

Multiple Choice

11. Answer: a Objective: 12

12. Answer: a Objective: 11

13. Answer: c Objective: 22

14. Answer: a Objective: 12

15. Answer: c Objective: 11

16. Answer: b Objective: 21

17. Answer: c Objective: 12

18. Answer: d Objective: 22

19. Answer: a Objective: 12

20. Answer: b Objective: 21

Short Answer

21. Answer:
The three landform regions of Southeast Asia are mountains in the north, a central region of flat plains and low plateaus, and a region that consists of thousands of islands.
Objective: 11

22. Answer:

The factors that made Southeast Asia an ideal site for European-owned plantations included a large population to supply inexpensive labor, tropical climates, and access to sea routes.

Objective: 12

Critical Thinking

23. Answer:

Possible answer: Southeast Asia has rich farmland, mineral wealth, and valuable tropical forests. Malaysia, Indonesia, and Thailand produce most of the world's supply of natural rubber. The region also produces and exports large amounts of rice, coffee, and other agricultural products, and valuable hardwoods, such as mahogany, ebony, and teak. The region holds the world's major tin deposits as well as large amounts of oil and other mineral and energy resources.

Southeast Asia faces many economic challenges, however. The continued cutting of the tropical forests has caused major environmental problems, leading some countries to institute logging bans. Poverty and lack of infrastructure are serious challenges for some countries. The recovery of the war-torn economies of Vietnam, Laos, and Cambodia may take many years before these countries can benefit from their potentially rich farmland and mineral resources. The effects of political and ethnic tension, as well as border conflicts and the pressure of refugees, are also causes for economic concern.

Objective: 12

24. Answer:

Answers will vary. Students who agree with the statement may point to the Vietnam War, fought between the Communist North Vietnamese and the U.S.-supported South Vietnamese. Students may also note that Communist governments came to power in Laos and Cambodia as well as in Vietnam. Students who disagree with the statement may point to Thailand and Burma, which have experienced tension caused by military governments and refugees but not by a struggle between Communist countries and non-Communist countries.

Objective: 22

25. Answer:

Possible answer: Myanmar is the name that was given to Burma by its military government in 1989. This government, which came to power in 1962, cut off foreign trade, created a socialist economy, has fought and driven out minority groups, and has suppressed democracy. The United States may be protesting against this government and its actions by not recognizing the name Myanmar.

Objective: 22

CHAPTER 45

TEST QUESTIONS

Matching

Match the term with its correct description. One term is not used.

a. sultanate
b. Singapore
c. *kampong*
d. sovereignty
e. Bali
f. archipelago

1. The name of a city, an island, and a nation in Southeast Asia

2. A large group of islands

3. An Indonesian traditional village or a slum surrounding an Indonesian city

4. Authority to rule

5. An island with rich cultural traditions that support Indonesia's tourist industry

Match the term with its correct description. One term is not used.

g. Java
h. Jakarta
i. Spratly
j. Kuala Lumpur
k. Luzon
l. Irian Jaya

6. The capital city of Malaysia

7. A group of islands in the South China Sea whose ownership has been disputed by the Philippines and other countries

8. The island on which most of the Philippines' people live

9. Indonesia's core island, which holds most of the country's industry and political power

10. The capital city of Indonesia

Multiple Choice

Circle the letter of the <u>best</u> answer.

11. To unify its population, the government of Indonesia is trying to
    a. increase the agricultural development on outlying islands.
    b. encourage more people to move to the islands of Java and Sumatra.
    c. persuade all citizens to use a national language.
    d. achieve political independence from colonial powers.

12. Like Indonesia, the Philippines
    a. was once a Spanish colony.
    b. has extensive petroleum deposits.
    c. is predominantly Muslim.
    d. produces sugarcane, coconuts, and tropical hardwoods.

13. Brunei has plans for agricultural expansion so that it can
    a. provide more citizens with jobs.
    b. attract foreign businesses.
    c. prepare for the depletion of its oil resources.
    d. make food exports its major source of income.

14. The products that can be made from Malaysia's major resources include all of the following except
    a. tires.   b. cans.   c. bread.   d. furniture.

15. Indonesia has a humid-tropical climate because
    a. its islands are covered with tropical forests.
    b. it is located at the junction of several tectonic plates.
    c. the region has several active volcanoes.
    d. all of its islands lie along the equator.

16. The economy of the Philippines depends on the export of
    a. petroleum.
    b. electrical products and textiles.
    c. rice and fish.
    d. minerals.

17. All of the following are problems facing the Philippines except
    a. deforestation.
    b. violent rebel movements.
    c. a lack of democratic government.
    d. a high foreign debt.

18. The largest Muslim population in the world is found in
    a. Indonesia.   b. the Philippines.
    c. Brunei.   d. Papua New Guinea.

19. The two main islands of the Philippines are
    a. Singapore and Brunei.   b. Java and Sumatra.
    c. Mindanao and Luzon.   d. Manila and Tagalog.

20. Indonesia is
    a. the most volcanic region on Earth.
    b. the world's most sparsely populated country.
    c. the wealthiest country of Southeast Asia.
    d. Asia's only ethnically uniform nation.

Short Answer

Answer the questions in the space provided.

21. How have Singapore and Brunei been able to provide their citizens with many social services?

    _____
    _____
    _____
    _____
    _____

22. Describe the cultural characteristics of the population of the Philippines.

_____
_____
_____
_____
_____

Critical Thinking

Write your answers on a separate sheet of paper.

23. Describe the effects of colonialism on the nations of island Southeast Asia.

24. Why do you think the populations of Indonesia and the Philippines are concentrated in a few areas?

25. What predictions can you make about the economy and living conditions of Malaysia in the year 2020?

CHAPTER 45

TEST ANSWERS

Matching

1. Answer: b Objective: 12

2. Answer: f Objective: 21

3. Answer: c Objective: 22

4. Answer: d Objective: 32

5. Answer: e Objective: 21

6. Answer: j Objective: 11

7. Answer: i Objective: 32

8. Answer: k Objective: 31

9. Answer: g Objective: 21

10. Answer: h Objective: 22

Multiple Choice

11. Answer: c Objective: 22

12. Answer: d Objective: 31

13. Answer: c Objective: 12

14. Answer: c Objective: 11

15. Answer: d Objective: 21

16. Answer: b Objective: 31

17. Answer: c Objective: 32

18. Answer: a Objective: 22

19. Answer: c Objective: 31

20. Answer: a Objective: 21

Short Answer

21. Answer:
    Singapore and Brunei are the smallest and richest nations of Southeast Asia. Singapore owes its prosperity to its productive population and its strategic location on the Strait of Malacca. It is one of the busiest ports in the world and the center of trade and banking in the region. Brunei is an oil-rich nation. The wealth of these two countries has paid for government-provided social services such as education, health care, and housing.

    Objective: 12

22. Answer:
Most Filipinos are of Malay origin, with strong Chinese and Spanish influences. About 85 percent of Filipinos are Roman Catholic; a small population of Muslims lives in the south. English is used in education and business; in addition, people speak the national language, Pilipino, and some speak an island language called Tagalog.

Objective: 31

Critical Thinking

23. Answer:
Possible answer: Many island nations of Southeast Asia were strongly affected by colonialism. The British governed Malaya until 1957, and Malaysia was formed in 1963. English is still commonly spoken in Malaysia today. Indonesia was ruled by the Dutch for more than 300 years, until it became independent in 1950. Tensions on the island of Timor, which was once split between the Dutch and the Portuguese, continue to this day. The Philippines, too, still shows strong evidence of its colonial past. The country was ruled by Spain for 300 years until the turn of the century; then it was controlled by the United States and then by Japan, until the islands achieved independence in 1946. The Spanish influence is seen in the islands' religion: more than 85 percent of the population is Roman Catholic. In addition, although the national language is Pilipino, the language widely used for education and business is English.

Objective: 22

24. Answer:
Possible answer: Although the countries are large, encompassing many islands, most Filipinos live on the island of Luzon, and most Indonesians live on the island of Java. These islands have the highest concentration of industry and therefore probably attract many people seeking jobs.

Objective: 21

25. Answer:
Possible answer: If Malaysia continues with its rapid rate of industrialization and the attraction of foreign investment, the country should continue to be fairly prosperous. Serious problems may occur, however, such as overcrowding and environmental pollution, as a result of the rapid industrialization.

Objective: 11

UNIT 9

TEST QUESTIONS

Matching

Match the term with its correct description. One term is not used.

a. Mekong
b. aquaculture
c. archipelago
d. Himalayas
e. Pinatubo
f. Huang He

   1. A major river of Southeast Asia

   2. A large group of islands, such as the thousands of Southeast Asia

   3. The world's highest mountain system, which forms a border between East and South Asia

   4. A Philippine volcano that erupted in 1991

   5. An important river in northern China

Match the term with its correct description. One term is not used.

g. Shinto
h. Hong Kong
i. Java
j. Taoism
k. Tonle Sap
l. communism

   6. Southeast Asia's largest lake, located in northwest Cambodia

   7. A busy port and large financial center that will be returned to China by the British in 1997

   8. The core island of Indonesia, where most of the country's people live

   9. A religion practiced in Japan

   10. An economic and political system adopted by several countries in East and Southeast Asia

Multiple Choice

Circle the letter of the <u>best</u> answer.

   11. The Silk Road was
       a. an important trade route that passed from China to Europe through Central Asia.
       b. a road traveled by Portuguese missionaries visiting Japan.
       c. the name given to the demilitarized zone between North and South Korea.
       d. the path taken by European traders through the Dutch East Indies.

12. Countries that have humid-continental climate regions include
    a. Vietnam, Burma, and Thailand.
    b. Indonesia, Taiwan, and the Philippines.
    c. Mongolia, Tibet, and Manchuria.
    d. China, North Korea, and Japan.

13. Two countries that were never colonized by European powers are
    a. Thailand and Japan.   b. Burma and Singapore.
    c. Indonesia and the Philippines.   d. Laos and Vietnam.

14. The languages spoken by most East and Southeast Asians
    a. are all related to each other.
    b. have effectively unified the region.
    c. are mainly Chinese, Japanese, and Korean.
    d. vary widely and often have regional dialects.

15. In this century, war has broken out between the northern Communist and southern democratic forces of both
    a. Japan and China.   b. Korea and Vietnam.
    c. Indonesia and Burma.   d. Malaysia and Taiwan.

16. Some of the mountains in Japan, the Philippines, and Indonesia
    a. are the region's most populated areas.
    b. provide a constant threat of volcanic eruptions.
    c. are the source of droughts that have kept these nations from being agriculturally productive.
    d. have effectively prevented invasions and colonization of these countries.

17. All of the following countries have Communist governments except
    a. China.   b. Brunei.   c. Laos.   d. North Korea.

18. Brunei and Singapore are two of East and Southeast Asia's
    a. driest countries.
    b. wealthiest countries.
    c. least politically stable countries.
    d. most ethnically diverse countries.

19. Most of the major population centers of East and Southeast Asia are located along coastlines or river valleys because
    a. these regions generally provide fertile, level farmland.
    b. inland areas are more vulnerable to attack by foreign invaders.
    c. monsoon winds do not affect the climate of the Asian mainland.
    d. most of the region's major religions are rooted in these areas.

20. The Republic of China was formed when
    a. Mao Zedong died and Deng Xiaoping came to power in China.
    b. Japan invaded China during the 1930s.
    c. Chinese Nationalists retreated to Taiwan after a war with Chinese Communists.
    d. Burma's military government drove out many Chinese people who were living in the country.

Short Answer

Answer the questions in the space provided.

21. Why do East and Southeast Asian farms tend to be small?

    _____
    _____
    _____
    _____
    _____

22. What major religions are practiced in East and Southeast Asia? For each religion you name, list an East or Southeast Asian country where it is widely practiced.

_____

_____

_____

_____

_____

Critical Thinking

Write your answers on a separate sheet of paper.

23. Explain the importance of East and Southeast Asia as a major region of the world.

24. Do you think that China has benefited from communism? Why or why not?

25. Laos banned the export of logs in 1990, in an effort to conserve its tropical forests. Do you think other countries of East and Southeast Asia should do the same? Explain.

UNIT 9

TEST ANSWERS

Matching

1.Answer: a Objective: 91

2.Answer: c Objective: 91

3.Answer: d Objective: 91

4.Answer: e Objective: 91

5.Answer: f Objective: 91

6.Answer: k Objective: 91

7.Answer: h Objective: 92

8.Answer: i Objective: 94

9.Answer: g Objective: 94

10.Answer: l Objective: 92

Multiple Choice

11.Answer: a Objective: 94

12.Answer: d Objective: 91

13.Answer: a Objective: 93

14.Answer: d Objective: 94

15.Answer: b Objective: 94

16.Answer: b Objective: 91

17.Answer: b Objective: 92

18.Answer: b Objective: 92

19.Answer: a Objective: 91

20.Answer: c Objective: 94

Short Answer

21.Answer:
Most of the region's many people are involved in agriculture. The amount of arable land, however, is limited by climate and terrain. Hence individual farms are small.
Objective: 91

22. Answer:
The major religions practiced in East and Southeast Asia are Islam (Indonesia, Malaysia, Brunei), Buddhism (Thailand, Burma, China, Laos, Cambodia, Vietnam, Mongolia), Taoism (China), Confucianism (China), Shinto (Japan), and Christianity (the Philippines, South Korea).

Objective: 92

Critical Thinking

23. Answer:
Possible answer: East and Southeast Asia is a major world region demographically, historically, economically, and culturally. Demographically, about one-third of the world's people live in the region, more than one billion of them in China alone. Historically, the region has been a center of international interest and conflict for several centuries. Many countries in the region were colonized by European or other foreign powers at one time. In addition, many countries, including Japan, Vietnam, the Philippines, and Korea, have been involved in wars with and among foreign powers, such as the Spanish-American War, World War II, the Korean War, and the Vietnam War.
The region also is important economically. Ever since the Silk Road was first traveled from China to Europe, trade has been an important enterprise in the region. Today, Japan is the second largest industrial power in the world. Many of its industries have been moved overseas. At the same time, Japan is experiencing competition from other newly industrialized Asian countries, such as China and South Korea. Together these countries have a major impact on world trade and politics. The region's rich cultural traditions, as well, have contributed a great deal to the world. For example, the region is the birthplace of several major world religions.

Objective: 93

24. Answer:
Answers will vary. Some students may argue that communism under the leadership of Deng Xiaoping has succeeded in feeding most of China's people, and that under Mao it provided equality for Chinese women. Others may argue that these gains are offset by the loss of political freedom under communism, pointing to events during the Cultural Revolution and the uprising at Tiananmen Square to support their point. Some students may also say that although Deng Xiaoping's government is Communist, much of China's economic advancement under this government has been a result of free-market type reforms rather than strictly Communist policies.

Objective: 92

25. Answer:
Answers will vary. Some students may point out that although Laos has banned the export of logs, illegal logging by corrupt military leaders continues. It might be possible to circumvent the law in other countries, too. Nevertheless, these students may argue, legislation may be the best assurance that the forests will be preserved. Students who do not believe that logging bans should be instituted may cite the importance of forestry to the economies of the region, claiming that the immediate needs of people are most important. Some students may suggest that a gradual ban rather than an immediate total ban might be a good compromise. Some students might also emphasize the need for reforestation programs.

Objective: 92

CHAPTER 46

TEST QUESTIONS

Matching

Match the term with its correct description. One term is not used.

a. Sikhism
b. tropical cyclone
c. monsoon
d. Hinduism
e. subcontinent
f. Green Revolution

1. A hurricane-like storm

2. A large landmass that is smaller than a continent

3. The major religion of India and Nepal

4. The introduction of new types of grains that produced high yields in South Asia

5. A religion whose followers are concentrated in India's northwestern Punjab region

Match the term with its correct description. One term is not used.

g. calico
h. Maldives
i. Dravidians
j. jute
k. Himalayas
l. indigo

6. A fine fabric woven from cotton and printed with colorful patterns

7. The world's highest and longest mountain system

8. A chain of low coral islands located southwest of India

9. The farming peoples who were driven south out of northern India by Aryan invaders

10. A plant fiber used to produce twine and coarse fabrics such as burlap

Multiple Choice

Circle the letter of the best answer.

11. The Himalayas were formed as a result of
    a. the formation of the Gondwanaland supercontinent.
    b. the collision between the Indian and Eurasian plates.
    c. volcanic eruptions and earthquakes in the South Asia region.
    d. rocky sediment deposited by rivers over thousands of years in northern India.

12. Future development in South Asia may be hindered by
   a. a slowdown in the production of Indian cotton.
   b. Pakistan's continuing struggle for independence.
   c. the failure of the Green Revolution's technology.
   d. a lack of petroleum and other industrial resources.

13. One thing that the Deccan Plateau and the Indo-Gangetic Plain have in common is
   a. extensive mineral resources.   b. a small population.
   c. fertile soil for agriculture.   d. occasional severe flooding.

14. Around 1500 B.C., the Indus Valley was conquered by
   a. Hindus.   b. Aryans.   c. Muslims.   d. Dravidians.

15. Sanskrit is the
   a. major religion practiced in Bangladesh.
   b. capital city of Sri Lanka.
   c. classical literary language of Hinduism.
   d. language spoken by Sikhs.

16. South Asia's three major rivers are
   a. the Indus, the Ganges, and the Brahmaputra.
   b. the Western Ghats, the Eastern Ghats, and the Bengal.
   c. the Thar, the Dharma, and the Mogul.
   d. the Aryan, the Dravidian, and the Mauryan.

17. All of the following climate types are found in South Asia except
   a. tropical savanna.   b. highland.
   c. marine west coast.   d. desert.

18. Existing farmland in South Asia is threatened by
   a. soil erosion and salinization.
   b. reforestation programs.
   c. pollution from chemical fertilizers.
   d. underpopulation of the land.

19. Just before Britain granted its South Asian colony independence in 1947, it
   a. closed all of India's textile factories.
   b. divided the subcontinent into the two countries of India and Pakistan.
   c. granted independence to the island of Ceylon (Sri Lanka).
   d. required all Muslims to convert to Hinduism or Christianity.

20. Mohandas Gandhi is an important figure in South Asian history because he
   a. was the leading supporter of the Green Revolution.
   b. instigated the Massacre at Amritsar in 1919.
   c. led the main independence movement in British India.
   d. established trade links between India and the Dutch East Indies.

Short Answer

Answer the questions in the space provided.

21. Why did violence break out in South Asia in the decades following independence?

   _____
   _____
   _____
   _____
   _____

22. Identify five agricultural challenges facing South Asia.

_____
_____
_____
_____
_____

Critical Thinking

Write your answers on a separate sheet of paper.

23. What factors have hindered industrialization in much of South Asia?

24. Evaluate the importance of the monsoon system to South Asia's economy.

25. If you were a government official in South Asia, what steps might you take to control population growth in the region?

CHAPTER 46

TEST ANSWERS

Matching

1. Answer: b   Objective: 12

2. Answer: e   Objective: 11

3. Answer: d   Objective: 21

4. Answer: f   Objective: 31

5. Answer: a   Objective: 21

6. Answer: g   Objective: 32

7. Answer: k   Objective: 11

8. Answer: h   Objective: 11

9. Answer: i   Objective: 21

10. Answer: j   Objective: 21

Multiple Choice

11. Answer: b   Objective: 11

12. Answer: d   Objective: 32

13. Answer: c   Objective: 11

14. Answer: b   Objective: 21

15. Answer: c   Objective: 21

16. Answer: a   Objective: 11

17. Answer: c   Objective: 12

18. Answer: a   Objective: 31

19. Answer: b   Objective: 22

20. Answer: c   Objective: 21

Short Answer

21. Answer:
Before granting independence, Britain divided the Indian subcontinent into India, which was primarily Hindu, and Pakistan, which was primarily Muslim. Many minorities, however, were left in both countries, and riots and massacres have occurred as a result of cultural conflicts. Violence also broke out in 1971 when East Pakistan, separated from West Pakistan by some 1,000 miles (1,609 km), broke away from West Pakistan to become Bangladesh.

Objective: 22

22.Answer:
Possible answers include small, inefficient farms, the high cost of fertilizers, a lack of mechanization, crop disease, natural disasters, a limited amount of land, soil erosion, and salinization.

Objective: 31

Critical Thinking

23.Answer:
Possible answer: South Asia's colonial history is partly responsible for the region's slow rate of industrialization. Hoping to forestall competition with their own industries, the British did not promote industry in South Asia during the colonial period. Rather, the region was a source of raw materials for British industry. Because of the emphasis on the production of raw materials and bans on Indian-made products, such as calicoes, some Indian industries declined under colonialism.

Another factor is South Asia's focus since independence on trying to feed its large population rather than on developing industry. In addition, internal political and social problems and natural disasters discouraged foreign investment. Although some industries have developed, mostly in the cities, future industrial development may be hindered by a lack of petroleum and other resources necessary for industrial growth.

Objective: 32

24.Answer:
Possible answer: Given current agricultural practices, the monsoon is vital to farmers in South Asia, and, as most South Asians are farmers, to the region's economy as a whole. If irrigation were developed, however, farmers might be less dependent on the monsoon cycle and agriculture might be able to thrive without it. Also, if the region became less agricultural and more industrial, the monsoon system would probably become less economically important.

Objective: 12

25.Answer:
Answers will vary. Some students might suggest that improving communication systems and educational programs designed to increase literacy might help control population growth in the region. Some students might also recommend making agricultural mechanization more accessible to rural farmers so that they could be less dependent on large families to help work fields.

Objective: 32

CHAPTER 47

TEST QUESTIONS

Matching

Match the term with its correct description. One term is not used.

a. Bombay
b. Indira Gandhi
c. Ganges
d. Jawaharlal Nehru
e. Narmada
f. Kashmir

1. A river on which a major hydroelectric-irrigation project is planned

2. India's largest city

3. The Indian river that is sacred to Hindus

4. A northwestern territory claimed by both India and Pakistan

5. India's prime minister who was assassinated by Sikhs in 1984

Match the term with its correct description. One term is not used.

g. caste system
h. sanctuary
i. Nicobar
j. Dravidian
k. Hindi
l. cottage industry

6. Islands located in the Bay of Bengal

7. An area in which endangered plants and animals are protected

8. The national language of India

9. A tradition by which India's people are divided into classes based on occupation

10. A form of business where workers make small consumer items in homes and small workshops

Multiple Choice

Circle the letter of the <u>best</u> answer.

11. In India, English is used widely
    a. in the northern part of the country.
    b. in the southern part of the country.
    c. in rural areas.
    d. in urban areas.

12. India's most severe environmental damage has been caused by
    a. industrial air pollution and ozone depletion.
    b. deforestation, overgrazing, and soil erosion.
    c. desertification and acid rain.
    d. global warming.

13. The plains near the Ganges River hold
    a. about three-fourths of India's population.
    b. more than one-third of India's population.
    c. about 10 percent of India's population.
    d. less than one percent of India's population.

14. All of the following have been created by the Indian government to increase agricultural production except for
    a. soil-erosion prevention programs.
    b. new irrigation systems.
    c. protective sanctuaries
    d. flood-control programs.

15. Nepal and Bhutan have served as buffer states between India and
    a. China.   b. Pakistan.
    c. Afghanistan.   d. Sri Lanka.

16. The climate of the central Deccan Plateau is
    a. highland.   b. steppe.   c. desert.   d. Mediterranean.

17. India's climates are strongly influenced by
    a. tropical cyclones.   b. the Thar Desert.
    c. the monsoon.   d. cold Arctic air.

18. The largest industrial area of northern India is
    a. New Delhi.   b. Madras.   c. Bombay.   d. Calcutta.

19. Recent violence in India has resulted from separatist movements and
    a. revolts by Buddhist sects.   b. Communist uprisings.
    c. Hindu nationalism.   d. the colonization of Nepal.

20. The fastest-growing sector of the Indian economy today is
    a. commercial agriculture.
    b. cotton textile mills.
    c. local and national government.
    d. private industry.

Short Answer

Answer the questions in the space provided.

21. Why are crop yields low in India, even though much of the country's soil is fertile?
    _____
    _____
    _____
    _____
    _____

22. What are India's major mineral and energy resources?
    _____
    _____
    _____
    _____
    _____

Critical Thinking

Write your answers on a separate sheet of paper.

23. Summarize the major differences between rural India and urban India.

24. How might the caste system have contributed to the fact that most people of India are farmers living on small incomes?

25. How will strengthening its infrastructure help India attract more foreign industry?

CHAPTER 47

TEST ANSWERS

Matching

1. Answer: e Objective: 22

2. Answer: a Objective: 32

3. Answer: c Objective: 11

4. Answer: f Objective: 11

5. Answer: b Objective: 31

6. Answer: i Objective: 11

7. Answer: h Objective: 12

8. Answer: k Objective: 31

9. Answer: g Objective: 32

10. Answer: l Objective: 32

Multiple Choice

11. Answer: d Objective: 31

12. Answer: b Objective: 12

13. Answer: b Objective: 11

14. Answer: c Objective: 21

15. Answer: a Objective: 11

16. Answer: b Objective: 11

17. Answer: c Objective: 11

18. Answer: a Objective: 32

19. Answer: c Objective: 31

20. Answer: d Objective: 22

Short Answer

21. Answer:
    A lack of modern farming methods and widespread irrigation has resulted in low crop yields in India. Most farmers cannot afford to buy modern equipment, fertilizers, and other items that might increase productivity.

    Objective: 21

22.Answer:
India's major mineral resources are iron ore, bauxite, coal, and some petroleum. The country's energy resources include uranium ore (which supports nuclear power) and hydroelectricity.

Objective: 22

Critical Thinking

23.Answer:
Possible answer: Rural India and urban India differ in a variety of social and economic ways. About three-quarters of all Indians live in rural villages, where they work as farmers. More than 30 percent of India's field workers do not own land, and about 60 percent of rural dwellers are illiterate. Rural villages often are isolated and lack adequate medical, educational, transportation, and communication services. Families are large. Some villages have cottage industries, where small consumer items are made. In rural India, the women are subordinate to men, and the caste system is still widespread.

   In Indian cities, literacy is generally higher, and women have more equality. The cities hold many educational opportunities as well as much industry. The English language and European customs are common, and the caste system is less important than in rural areas. The cities have a growing middle class, but most urban dwellers remain poor. Many are homeless, while others live in slums in poor conditions. Government family planning programs have had greater success in urban areas than in rural areas. The urban population, however, continues to grow as migration from rural areas increases.

Objective: 32

24.Answer:
Possible answer: The caste system remains a part of Hindu life, especially in the rural villages where most of the people of India live. According to the caste system, a person born into an occupational class (or caste) cannot move into another. Therefore, people who are born into a rural farm family cannot hope to change their occupation or improve their standard of living if they remain in the village.

Objective: 32

25.Answer:
Possible answer: Unless the country's transportation and communication systems become more modern and reliable, foreign industries will be reluctant to invest in India. Businesses need to transport raw materials and finished goods quickly. In addition, to be competitive, businesses also need to receive news about and communicate with other businesses in the region, country, and around the world.

Objective: 22

CHAPTER 48

TEST QUESTIONS

Matching

Match the term with its correct description. One term is not used.

a. Tarai
b. Colombo
c. cease-fire
d. storm surge
e. Tamil
f. partition

1. To divide, as South Asia was divided by the British

2. A rise in tide level that occurs as a storm approaches the coast, causing seawater to flood over the land

3. An agreement to halt active hostility

4. A low, tropical plain in Nepal

5. One of Sri Lanka's two major culture groups

Match the term with its correct description. One term is not used.

g. Karakoram
h. Dhaka
i. graphite
j. Punjabi
k. limestone
l. Indus

6. The capital and largest city of Bangladesh

7. The mountain range that forms Pakistan's northern border with China

8. Pakistan's largest ethnic group

9. The name of the river valley where most of Pakistan's agriculture and large population are located

10. A mineral, found in Sri Lanka, that is used in pencils

Multiple Choice

Circle the letter of the <u>best</u> answer.

11. India and Pakistan continue to disagree about the status of
    a. Kathmandu.
    b. Bhutan.
    c. Baluchistan.
    d. Kashmir.

12. Pakistan's major export crop is
    a. rice.   b. corn.   c. cotton.   d. soybeans.

13. In an attempt to improve the country's economy, the government of Pakistan has done all of
    the following except
    a. improve the nation's roads and communications systems.
    b. promote the privatization of state-owned industries.
    c. attempt to attract foreign investment to increase export earnings.
    d. increase the amount of oil imported into the country.

14. The majority of the people of Bhutan are
    a. Tamils.   b. Buddhists.   c. Hindus.   d. Sinhalese.

15. Important to Nepal's economy are tourists, most of whom visit the country to
    a. shop.   b. hike.   c. swim.   d. meditate.

16. The world's largest exporter of tea is
    a. Sri Lanka.   b. Pakistan.
    c. the Maldives.   d. Bangladesh.

17. The monsoon season can cause problems in Bangladesh because
    a. wheat, the nation's major export crop, cannot survive flooding.
    b. its heavy summer rains often flood the highly populated low plains and river deltas.
    c. industry in the cities is less productive during the rainy season.
    d. its unpredictable weather patterns discourage tourists from visiting the country.

18. Most Nepalese live in or near the capital city of
    a. Colombo.   b. Dhaka.   c. Karachi.   d. Kathmandu.

19. In 1971 East Pakistan
    a. became an Islamic republic based on Islamic law.
    b. invaded and conquered West Pakistan.
    c. became the independent country of Bangladesh.
    d. adopted Urdu as its official language.

20. The country whose only neighbors are India and Burma is
    a. Bhutan.   b. Nepal.   c. Pakistan.   d. Bangladesh.

Short Answer

Answer the questions in the space provided.

21. What is the major challenge facing Bangladesh today?
    _____
    _____
    _____
    _____
    _____

22. Identify Pakistan's three landform regions.
    _____
    _____
    _____
    _____
    _____

Critical Thinking

Write your answers on a separate sheet of paper.

23. Discuss the theme of human-environment interaction in the countries of the Indian perimeter. How have people in these countries adapted to their physical environments? How have they changed these environments? Use specific examples.

24. How is Bhutan similar to and different from Nepal?

25. Ethnic groups within both Kashmir and Sri Lanka came into violent conflict with each other once independence was granted by Britain. Why do you think this is so? Give examples to support your answer.

CHAPTER 48

TEST ANSWERS

Matching

1. Answer: f Objective: 11

2. Answer: d Objective: 31

3. Answer: c Objective: 12

4. Answer: a Objective: 21

5. Answer: e Objective: 42

6. Answer: h Objective: 32

7. Answer: g Objective: 11

8. Answer: j Objective: 12

9. Answer: l Objective: 11

10. Answer: i Objective: 41

Multiple Choice

11. Answer: d Objective: 12

12. Answer: c Objective: 12

13. Answer: d Objective: 12

14. Answer: b Objective: 22

15. Answer: b Objective: 21

16. Answer: a Objective: 41

17. Answer: b Objective: 32

18. Answer: d Objective: 21

19. Answer: c Objective: 12

20. Answer: d Objective: 31

Short Answer

21. Answer:
    The major challenge facing Bangladesh today is how to feed, educate, and employ its more than 110 million people. As the population continues to grow, there will be less space and fewer resources. At its present rate of growth, the population of Bangladesh will double within 35 years.

    Objective: 32

22. Answer:
    Pakistan's three landform regions are the mountains in the north, the deserts in the east and west, and the Indus River Valley.

    Objective: 11

Critical Thinking

23. Answer:
    Answers will vary. Possible examples of adaptation include settlement and agriculture in Pakistan's Indus River valley, Nepal's use of its mountainous terrain to attract tourists to earn income, Bangladesh's growing of crops year-round enabled by a humid-tropical climate, and the Maldives' earning much of its income from fish products, available from the surrounding ocean. Possible examples of change include deforestation and overgrazing in Pakistan, deforestation in Nepal and Bangladesh, and pollution in Bangladesh's factory towns.

    Objective: 12

24. Answer:
    Unlike Nepal, whose economy depends largely on tourism, Bhutan has been isolated for much of its history. As a result, Bhutan has managed to avoid many of the deforestation problems that plague Nepal. Most Nepalese are Hindus, while most of Bhutan's people are Buddhists. Both countries have agriculturally productive regions, though Bhutan is more self-sufficient in food production. Subsistence farming is widely practiced in both countries. Both countries are mountainous and landlocked and depend on India for most trade and foreign aid. Both are monarchies, although Nepal's king has limited power.

    Objective: 22

25. Answer:
    Possible answer: Under colonialism, tensions probably existed but were suppressed either by the colonists or by the groups themselves, particularly as they may have banded together in a struggle to achieve independence from their colonial rulers. Some students may say that, with independence, each group saw a chance to have power and was not willing to share that power with other groups. In Sri Lanka, for example, the larger group, the Sinhalese, discriminated against the Tamils after independence. In Kashmir, much of the violence has stemmed from the way the region was divided just prior to independence.

    Objective: 42

UNIT 10

TEST QUESTIONS

Matching

Match the term with its correct description. One term is not used.

a. Brahmin
b. storm surge
c. Hindu
d. Brahmaputra
e. Mauryan
f. tropical cyclone

1. A hurricane-like storm that strikes South Asia in the spring and fall

2. A major South Asian river

3. A rise in tide level that occurs as a storm approaches the coast

4. An Indian empire that spread Buddhism throughout much of Asia

5. A member of the highest class of India's caste system

Match the term with its correct description. One term is not used.

g. Indira Gandhi
h. Kathmandu
i. monsoon
j. Mohandas Gandhi
k. cardamom
l. Tamil

6. Seasonal winds that strongly influence the climates of South Asia

7. The prime minister of India from 1964 to 1984

8. The person who led the main Indian struggle for independence from Britain

9. The capital city of Nepal

10. An ethnic group of Sri Lanka

Multiple Choice

Circle the letter of the <u>best</u> answer.

11. The South Asian nation with an Islamic government is
    a. India.   b. Sri Lanka.   c. Pakistan.   d. Nepal.

12. The Himalayas are the source of
    a. minerals used to process jute for export.
    b. the major rivers of South Asia.
    c. the fertile soils of the Maldives.
    d. South Asia's major religions.

13. An important source of energy produced in both India and Pakistan is
    a. solar energy.   b. nuclear power.
    c. hydroelectricity.   d. petroleum.

14. The South Asian countries in which Hindus form a majority are
    a. Pakistan and Bangladesh.   b. India and Nepal.
    c. Sri Lanka and Bhutan.   d. Kashmir and the Maldives.

15. The factor that will probably have the greatest impact on the future of South Asia is the
    a. exploration and development of natural-gas deposits.
    b. abandonment of the Green Revolution.
    c. rate of population growth in the region.
    d. discovery of large gold deposits in Pakistan.

16. During India's colonial period, the raw material most valued by Great Britain was
    a. rice.   b. wool.   c. spices.   d. cotton.

17. Unlike South Asia's river valleys, the Deccan Plateau
    a. does not have fertile soil to support agriculture.
    b. is affected by the fall and spring monsoon winds.
    c. has fertile soil made from weathered volcanic rocks.
    d. has a high population density.

18. About half of Pakistan's exports are produced by
    a. mining.   b. agriculture.
    c. petroleum reserves.   d. heavy industries.

19. The caste system in India has led to
    a. discrimination and violence toward the untouchables.
    b. civil war between the Brahmins and the Vaisyas.
    c. agricultural reforms and pollution controls.
    d. strengthening the country's economy.

20. Before 1971 Bangladesh was
    a. a Dutch colony.   b. Burma's closest ally.
    c. a Communist country.   d. East Pakistan.

Short Answer

Answer the questions in the space provided.

21. How does the monsoon affect South Asia's climate?

    _____
    _____
    _____
    _____
    _____

22. In South Asia today, why is there little suitable land left to develop for agriculture?

    _____
    _____
    _____
    _____
    _____

Critical Thinking

Write your answers on a separate sheet of paper.

23. How might South Asia make the best use of its resources and foreign aid?

24. What do Pakistan and Bangladesh have in common? How are they different?

25. Which of the South Asian countries has the greatest potential for future prosperity, in your opinion? Why?

UNIT 10

TEST ANSWERS

Matching

1. Answer: f Objective: 101

2. Answer: d Objective: 101

3. Answer: b Objective: 101

4. Answer: e Objective: 102

5. Answer: a Objective: 104

6. Answer: i Objective: 101

7. Answer: g Objective: 102

8. Answer: j Objective: 102

9. Answer: h Objective: 104

10. Answer: l Objective: 102

Multiple Choice

11. Answer: c Objective: 104

12. Answer: b Objective: 101

13. Answer: c Objective: 103

14. Answer: b Objective: 102

15. Answer: c Objective: 104

16. Answer: d Objective: 102

17. Answer: c Objective: 103

18. Answer: b Objective: 103

19. Answer: a Objective: 104

20. Answer: d Objective: 102

Short Answer

21. Answer:
    The monsoon strongly influences South Asia's climate. The summer monsoon pulls moist air inland, causing high humidity, heavy rains, and thunderstorms. In the winter, the monsoon winds create a dry, warm climate.

    Objective: 101

22. Answer:

The region's large population, most of whom are farmers, already use most of the region's fertile lands. Existing farmlands, meanwhile, are threatened by soil erosion and salinization. As populations grow even larger, so do demands for farmland and wood. Thus, forests are cut down, leading eventually to increased flooding and loss of arable soil.

Objective: 104

Critical Thinking

23. Answer:

Possible response: Foreign aid and the water and mineral resources of South Asia could be used to solve one of the region's major problems—meeting the needs of a growing population. For India and Pakistan, additional income could be earned by exporting industrial resources, such as coal, iron ore, and natural gas. This income, along with foreign aid, could be applied to rural agricultural development projects. New irrigation projects could increase arable land in dry areas. Investments in flood-control and soil-erosion prevention projects might further raise agricultural productivity; flood control might be particularly valuable in Bangladesh, where monsoons have proven most destructive. Improved agricultural methods could help yield greater crops to feed more people. Water resources could be used not only for irrigation projects, but also to provide hydroelectric power to support growing industries. These industries might generate income that could be used to import goods the region cannot produce itself.

Objective: 103

24. Answer:

Possible answer: Most of the people of Pakistan and Bangladesh live in fertile river valleys. Rivers are important to both countries for agriculture, to Pakistan for hydroelectricity, and to Bangladesh for transportation. Deforestation is a serious problem in both countries. In addition, in both countries most people are Muslims and work as farmers. Both countries are also experiencing tremendous population growth.

Pakistan, however, has mountains and deserts, while most of Bangladesh consists of low flood plains. Bangladesh is more subject to natural disasters than is Pakistan. Pakistan has had a tense relationship with India, especially regarding the status of Kashmir. Bangladesh is surrounded on three sides by India, with whom its relations are peaceful.

Objective: 104

25. Answer:

Answers will vary. Most students will probably say that India and Pakistan have the greatest potential for future prosperity. They are not isolated, like Sri Lanka, Nepal, and Bhutan. Nor are they subject to frequent natural disasters, like Bangladesh. India and Pakistan have a variety of natural resources and potential energy resources, which could help attract foreign investment.

Objective: 103

CHAPTER 49

TEST QUESTIONS

Matching

Match the term with its correct description. One term is not used.

a. biogeography
b. eucalyptus
c. Nullarbor Plain
d. Great Barrier Reef
e. Great Dividing Range
f. marsupial

1. A kind of mammal that carries its young in a pouch

2. Earth's flattest landform region, which lies along the southern edge of Australia's Western Plateau

3. The highest part of Australia's Eastern Highlands

4. The type of plant that dominates Australia

5. The study of the geographic distribution of plants and animals

Match the term with its correct description. One term is not used.

g. artesian well
h. Sydney
i. endemic species
j. hinterland
k. Murray-Darling
l. alien species

6. Plants or animals that originate only in a particular geographic region

7. Plants and animals introduced to a region by humans from a different region

8. A place where water rises to the surface without being pumped

9. Australia's oldest and largest city and the capital of New South Wales

10. Australia's only major river system

Multiple Choice

Circle the letter of the <u>best</u> answer.

11. About half of Australia, mostly in the continent's interior, has a
    a. desert climate.
    b. steppe climate.
    c. marine-west-coast climate.
    d. tropical-savanna climate.

12. Australia is a major exporter of
    a. citrus fruits, olives, and copper.
    b. rice, soybeans, and oil.
    c. wool, wheat, and beef.
    d. mutton, apples, and tropical fruits.

13. The factor that presents the greatest challenge to Australia's industries is
    a. an unskilled workforce.   b. a weak transportation network.
    c. a small consumer population.   d. foreign competition.

14. Kangaroos and koalas in Australia are examples of
    a. alien species.   b. biogeographical species.
    c. distributed species.   d. endemic species.

15. Australia's three largest cities and most of its population are found in the
    a. Northern Territory.   b. country's southeastern corner.
    c. continent's interior.   d. island state of Tasmania.

16. Australia faces all of the following environmental challenges except
    a. forest destruction.
    b. smog in urban areas.
    c. the extinction of the kangaroo.
    d. wind erosion of topsoil.

17. All of the following industries are growing rapidly in Australia except
    a. services.   b. the iron industry.
    c. the entertainment industry.   d. tourism.

18. If you lived in Adelaide or Perth, you could expect
    a. hot desert conditions all year long.
    b. dry, sunny summers and mild, rainy winters.
    c. periods of drought and flooding.
    d. warm, rainy weather all year long.

19. Most of Australia's trade is conducted with
    a. South America.   b. Asian countries.
    c. European Community nations.   d. New Zealand.

20. The Great Barrier Reef is located
    a. off the northeastern coast of Queensland.
    b. in the Outback region.
    c. off the northern coast of Tasmania.
    d. south of Brisbane and Canberra.

Short Answer

Answer the questions in the space provided.

21. How does the Great Dividing Range affect Australia's climates?

    _____
    _____
    _____
    _____
    _____

22. How has Australia become self-sufficient in food with such limited arable land and water resources?

_____
_____
_____
_____
_____

Critical Thinking

Write your answers on a separate sheet of paper.

23. Describe Australia's population geography. How is the population distributed? What is its cultural composition?

24. What industries might Australians develop in the future without causing environmental damage? Which industries should not be further developed? Explain your choices.

25. Imagine that major oil deposits were discovered underneath the Great Barrier Reef. Would you support the development of these oil deposits? Why or why not?

CHAPTER 49

TEST ANSWERS

Matching

1. Answer: f Objective: 12

2. Answer: c Objective: 11

3. Answer: e Objective: 11

4. Answer: b Objective: 12

5. Answer: a Objective: 12

6. Answer: i Objective: 12

7. Answer: l Objective: 12

8. Answer: g Objective: 11

9. Answer: h Objective: 31

10. Answer: k Objective: 11

Multiple Choice

11. Answer: a Objective: 11

12. Answer: c Objective: 21

13. Answer: d Objective: 22

14. Answer: d Objective: 12

15. Answer: b Objective: 31

16. Answer: c Objective: 32

17. Answer: b Objective: 22

18. Answer: b Objective: 11

19. Answer: b Objective: 22

20. Answer: a Objective: 11

Short Answer

21. Answer:
    The Great Dividing Range is in the path of the southeast trade winds. Moisture falls on the windward slopes, causing the narrow humid climate regions of the east coast of the continent. The range, however, acts as a barrier preventing moist Pacific winds from reaching the leeward rain-shadow side of the range and the continent's interior. Hence, the interior and western parts of the country have dry climates.

    Objective: 11

22. Answer:

Australia's small population and diverse climate regions partly explain why the country is agriculturally self-sufficient. Australians also make efficient use of the limited arable land.

Objective: 21

Critical Thinking

23. Answer:

Population Distribution: More than 85 percent of all Australians live in urban areas. Each state and territory has a nodal city and seaport, where most of that state's or territory's people live, and suburbs fan out into the hinterland. Australia's three largest cities—Sydney, Melbourne, and Brisbane—are located in the southeastern corner of Australia. New South Wales, where Sydney is located, is Australia's most populous state.

Cultural Composition: The Aborigines were Australia's first inhabitants; today, only about one percent of the population is made up of this group. They have been granted some land in the Northern Territory, but most Aborigines live in poverty in urban areas. Immigration has had a major influence on Australia's population geography. The British and Irish settlers of the colonial era were later joined by other European immigrants, particularly from Greece and Italy. Australia's population has doubled in the last 40 years, largely due to immigration from Asian countries such as Vietnam, Malaysia, China, and Cambodia.

Objective: 31

24. Answer:

Answers will vary. Some students may say that by investing in advertising the scenic beauty of the continent, Australia can attract tourists and moviemakers, thereby increasing its revenues and preserving the environment. Other students, however, may point out that tourism can also have negative environmental effects. Expansion of the wool, cattle, and agricultural industries might cause a further drain on the limited water resources of the country and cause further deforestation. Any increased heavy industry would probably add to air and water pollution.

Objective: 32

25. Answer:

Answers will vary. Some students may say that because Australia is not self-sufficient in oil, the country would be wise to develop the new deposits even if the reef is exposed to the risk of environmental damage from oil spills or is disrupted by the drilling. Other students may say that even though Australia is not self-sufficient in oil, it almost is and has many other mineral and energy resources that could be developed instead. These students may argue that the preservation of the Great Barrier Reef, one of Earth's most complex ecosystems, is more important than further improving the economy of a nation that is already fairly prosperous.

Objective: 21

CHAPTER 50

TEST QUESTIONS

Matching

Match the term with its correct description. One term is not used.

a. Antarctic Convergence Zone
b. commonwealth
c. trust territory
d. Exclusive Economic Zone (EEZ)
e. Oceania
f. Pacific Ring of Fire

  1. The current political status of the Northern Mariana Islands, which makes residents U.S. citizens

  2. The area in which New Zealand is located, making the nation vulnerable to earthquakes and volcanic eruptions

  3. The Pacific region, most of which is water

  4. An area off the coast of a country, in which marine resources are controlled by that country

  5. The ocean region in which the cold Southern Ocean meets the warmer middle-latitude waters

Match the term with its correct description. One term is not used.

g. Maori
h. Pidgin
i. West Wind Drift
j. atoll
k. katabatic wind
l. polar desert

  6. A trade language based on English and spoken in Papua New Guinea

  7. A ring of small islands built up on a coral reef surrounding a shallow lagoon

  8. A Polynesian people who settled New Zealand between the tenth and fifth centuries

  9. A rapid flow of dense cold air down the slopes of high mountains or ice caps

  10. The world's largest ocean current, which flows clockwise around Antarctica

Multiple Choice

Circle the letter of the <u>best</u> answer.

  11. Much of New Zealand is made up of
      a. atolls.
      c. mountains and hills.
      b. flat plains.
      d. polar deserts.

12. Most of New Zealand's electricity is supplied by
    a. coal and natural gas.
    b. geothermal and hydroelectric power.
    c. solar and tidal power.
    d. nuclear power and oil.

13. A serious problem experienced by many Pacific islands is
    a. a severe trade deficit.
    b. a harsh climate that discourages tourism.
    c. the inability to control their own marine resources.
    d. a lack of trading partners.

14. Because of Antarctica's severe climate,
    a. the continent is in total darkness for several months each year.
    b. it is impossible for humans to travel to the South Pole.
    c. researchers believe that the continent has no mineral resources.
    d. tundra vegetation is the only plant life found on the continent.

15. In 1769, New Zealand was claimed by James Cook for
    a. Great Britain.   b. the United States.
    c. Australia.   d. France.

16. Melanesia's dominant exports are
    a. meat products.   b. steel and aluminum.
    c. citrus fruits.   d. minerals.

17. The only people found in Antarctica today are
    a. the native Maori population.   b. scientific researchers.
    c. miners.   d. Pacific islanders.

18. More than 85 percent of New Zealanders live
    a. along the Tasman coast.   b. in urban areas.
    c. on dairy farms and ranches.   d. in the Southern Alps.

19. A populous Pacific nation, where more than 700 languages are spoken, is
    a. Hawaii.   b. Micronesia.
    c. Papua New Guinea.   d. New Zealand.

20. The Pacific island region that forms a triangle with corners at New Zealand, Hawaii, and Easter Island is
    a. Polynesia.   b. Vanuatu.
    c. Micronesia.   d. Melanesia.

Short Answer

Answer the questions in the space provided.

21. Why do the Pacific high islands support larger populations than the low islands?

    _____
    _____
    _____
    _____
    _____

22. Why do most New Zealanders live on North Island?

    _____
    _____
    _____
    _____
    _____

Critical Thinking

Write your answers on a separate sheet of paper.

23. Describe the political, cultural, and economic relationships that the Pacific islands and New Zealand have had with foreign nations.

24. Why do you think the United States and other countries have wanted to control territory in the Pacific?

25. Do you think large human settlements will someday exist on Antarctica?

CHAPTER 50

TEST ANSWERS

Matching

1. Answer: b Objective: 11

2. Answer: f Objective: 21

3. Answer: e Objective: 11

4. Answer: d Objective: 12

5. Answer: a Objective: 31

6. Answer: h Objective: 12

7. Answer: j Objective: 11

8. Answer: g Objective: 22

9. Answer: k Objective: 31

10. Answer: i Objective: 31

Multiple Choice

11. Answer: c Objective: 21

12. Answer: b Objective: 22

13. Answer: a Objective: 12

14. Answer: d Objective: 31

15. Answer: a Objective: 22

16. Answer: d Objective: 12

17. Answer: b Objective: 32

18. Answer: b Objective: 22

19. Answer: c Objective: 12

20. Answer: a Objective: 12

Short Answer

21. Answer:
Most high islands were formed by volcanoes rising from the sea or as continental fragments. They have fresh water, goods soils, and forest resources. Low islands, meanwhile, lie mostly just above sea level and are made of coral. Their few resources, limited fresh water, thin soils, and few trees cannot support large populations.
Objective: 11

22. Answer:
Most New Zealanders live on North Island because most of the country's industry, agriculture, and the largest cities are located there. The climate of North Island is milder than that of South Island, and its rolling hills and plains are more suitable for agriculture than are South Island's high mountains. Also, geothermal energy on North Island provides a source of power.

Objective: 22

Critical Thinking

23. Answer:
Answers will vary. The Pacific Islands: The first European explorers arrived in the Pacific islands in the sixteenth century. Beginning in the late eighteenth century, the European powers claimed territory in the region. During the ensuing colonial period, Europeans had a significant impact on the region. Many islanders were converted to Christianity, and many workers from India and China settled in the region. In the twentieth century, Japanese, U.S., and other forces invaded much of the islands' territory. As a result, many of the islands were devastated during World War II. After the war, some island groups became trust territories. Some later chose their own form of government, while others, such as Tahiti, Guam, Midway, and Wake Island, remained territories of foreign countries. The Northern Mariana Islands are a commonwealth of the United States. Economically, many Pacific island nations depend on the larger nations of the Pacific Rim for support. Many islanders are concerned that island cultures are changing and disappearing due to foreign influences.
New Zealand: New Zealand was claimed for Great Britain in 1769, and British settlements were established in the 1840s. Since 1852 it has had self-government, though it remains a member of the British Commonwealth. New Zealand has tried to maintain good relations with all countries because of its dependence on foreign trade. Since the formation of the European Community, New Zealand ceased being dependent on British markets. Its major trade partners are now Japan, Australia, and the United States, as well as the EC.

Objective: 11

24. Answer:
Possible answer: Possession and control of Pacific islands means control over the Pacific trade routes between Asia and North and South America. Territories in the region also provide strategic sites for military bases.

Objective: 11

25. Answer:
Possible answer: Except for the few researchers who work in scientific research stations, it is unlikely that large numbers of people could live in Antarctica. The extreme climate will not support human settlements. The ban against mining and drilling for oil make it unlikely that settlers would want to move there.

Objective: 32

UNIT 11

TEST QUESTIONS

Matching

Match the term with its correct description. One term is not used.

a. James Cook
b. Maoris
c. atoll
d. Abel Tasman
e. Aborigines
f. artesian well

  1. A ring of small islands built up on a coral reef surrounding a shallow lagoon

  2. A Dutch explorer who was the first European to sight New Zealand

  3. The native peoples of Australia

  4. A place where groundwater rises to the surface in Australia

  5. The peoples who settled in New Zealand between 900 and 1400.

Match the term with its correct description. One term is not used.

g. Guam
h. Vinson Massif
i. Polynesia
j. Ayers Rock
k. Southern Alps
l. Melanesia

  6. An island group in the Pacific that includes New Guinea and Fiji

  7. A huge landform in Australia, located south of the Macdonnell Ranges

  8. A mountain range in New Zealand

  9. A high island in the Pacific that is a U.S. territory

  10. An island group in the Pacific that includes Tonga and Samoa

Multiple Choice

Circle the letter of the best answer.

  11. More than half of Australia is covered by the
     a. Western Plateau.   b. Cape York Peninsula.
     c. Eastern Highlands.   d. Great Dividing Range.

12. In both Australia and New Zealand,
    a. there are abundant mineral resources.
    b. severe water shortages are common.
    c. native peoples enjoy a high standard of living.
    d. most people live in urban areas.

13. A major economic activity in Australia's Outback is
    a. rice growing.   b. dairy farming.
    c. mining.   d. manufacturing.

14. People are concerned that Australia's Great Barrier Reef may be
    a. subject to earthquakes and tidal waves.
    b. settled by immigrants from Asia.
    c. damaged by tourism and offshore oil drilling.
    d. used as a hunting ground for endemic species.

15. Low islands in the Pacific were formed from
    a. ocean volcanoes.   b. continental fragments.
    c. artesian wells.   d. coral reefs.

16. The first settlers of New Zealand were the
    a. Dutch.   b. Moa hunters.
    c. Melanesians.   d. Aborigines.

17. One reason most of Australia receives little rain is that
    a. stable air of the subtropical high-pressure system prevents rain from reaching many
       areas.
    b. the Great Australian Bight prevents rain from reaching the interior.
    c. little water evaporates from the surface of the continent.
    d. the rain-shadow side of the Southern Alps blocks rain from the windward side.

18. Many Pacific islands protect their offshore resources by
    a. establishing military bases.
    b. claiming Exclusive Economic Zones.
    c. limiting tourist travel.
    d. establishing scientific research stations.

19. New Zealand and New Guinea are both
    a. high continental islands.
    b. located in the Great Australian Bight.
    c. low islands.
    d. possessions of Great Britain.

20. Most of Australia's traditional industries are
    a. being privatized.   b. being nationalized.
    c. increasingly prosperous.   d. in decline.

Short Answer

Answer the questions in the space provided.

21. What effects did European settlement have on Australia's Aborigines?
    _____
    _____
    _____
    _____
    _____

22. What are New Zealand's major exports and imports?

_____
_____
_____
_____
_____
_____

Critical Thinking

Write your answers on a separate sheet of paper.

23. What issues confront Australia, New Zealand, and the Pacific islands today and for the future?

24. Identify three ways in which Australia is similar to the United States.

25. Should Antarctica continue to be off-limits to mining? Why or why not?

UNIT 11

TEST ANSWERS

Matching

1. Answer: c Objective: 111

2. Answer: d Objective: 117

3. Answer: e Objective: 112

4. Answer: f Objective: 113

5. Answer: b Objective: 112

6. Answer: l Objective: 111

7. Answer: j Objective: 111

8. Answer: k Objective: 111

9. Answer: g Objective: 111

10. Answer: i Objective: 111

Multiple Choice

11. Answer: a Objective: 111

12. Answer: d Objective: 112

13. Answer: c Objective: 113

14. Answer: c Objective: 115

15. Answer: d Objective: 111

16. Answer: b Objective: 112

17. Answer: a Objective: 111

18. Answer: b Objective: 113

19. Answer: a Objective: 111

20. Answer: d Objective: 113

Short Answer

21. Answer:
The Aborigines used to be a nomadic hunting-and-gathering people. After Europeans arrived in Australia, this way of life disappeared, and many Aborigines died of diseases introduced by the Europeans. Today, most Aborigines are poor and live in urban areas. Their life expectancy is 20 years less than that of other Australians. They are, however, gaining back some of the rights they lost during European settlement.

Objective: 112

22. Answer:
New Zealand is nearly self-sufficient in food production. It produces a variety of industrial goods and has a variety of energy resources. The nation exports agricultural crops, such as wool, lamb, beef, butter, cheese, apples, and kiwifruit. New Zealand is not rich in mineral resources, however, and must import oil and most manufactured goods.

Objective: 114

Critical Thinking

23. Answer:
Possible answer: In Australia, protection of the continent's unique wildlife is a major source of concern and controversy. Protection of fragile ecosystems, such as the Great Barrier Reef, from tourism and offshore oil drilling, is likely to continue to be an issue. Status of the Aborigines is another issue, as is immigration growth. Environmental concerns, largely spurred by rapid population growth and economic development, will continue to be important issues in the future. Specifically, these include urban smog, mining, damming of rivers, forest destruction, salinity, and wind erosion of topsoil.

In the Pacific islands, future issues are likely to concern the islands' severe trade deficits and the effects of rapid acculturation on native cultures. In New Zealand, trade issues are likely to be important, as they are for all the nations and territories of the Pacific region.

Objective: 113

24. Answer:
Possible answers: Both Australia and the United States are developed, industrialized countries. Each nation was originally settled as a colony. Many residents of both countries are immigrants or descendents of immigrants. The original, indigenous population of each country was subjugated, and many of the descendants of the indigenous people now live in poor circumstances. Each country is largely self-sufficient in food production. Both Australia and the United States face environmental problems.

Objective: 117

25. Answer:
Answers will vary. Some students will probably say that Antarctica should continue to be off-limits to mining. The ecosystem of the continent is very fragile, and mining might destroy the animals and plants in the region. Mining might also interfere with some of the important scientific research being conducted in Antarctica. Other students may argue that Antarctica should be mined, since its natural resources are valuable and needed, and the country is not likely to be settled.

Objective: 115